Osceola belonged to a tribe of Creek I
ns that lived in southern Georgia. S
he War of 1812, these Indians ·
1.   ·tir   ·nds ;

As the war progressed, Osceola and his warriors were driven deeper into the Everglades
·he Big Cypress Swamp. The Indians
       ·h·es with ·var·a·rt, so that
                     ·o·ly

Osceola

Young Seminole Indian

Illustrated by Robert Doremus

Osceola

Young Seminole Indian

By Electa Clark

*To Gertude Hecker Winders
who has generously given encouragement
and help to many authors*

Illustrations

Full Pages

Numerous smaller illustrations

Contents

Books by Electa Clark

OSCEOLA: YOUNG SEMINOLE INDIAN
ROBERT PEARY: BOY OF THE NORTH POLE

Osceola

Young Seminole Indian

Wildcat!

"LITTLE FOX, I like this new country," said the Indian boy. "I'm glad everybody in our town decided to move here together."

Two little brown-skinned boys walked side by side in a long line of Indians. Warriors carrying bows and arrows or carrying rifles led the march. Some were on foot and some rode horseback. Behind them came women and children.

Little Fox said, "I like it here too. What is this new land called?"

"Florida."

The file of Indians walked through a forest of tall pines. It was not a thick forest. The

11

trees grew so far apart that the boys could look up at the clear blue sky.

"I wish I could ride," Little Fox said. "This load is heavy." He wore a knapsack made of deerskin. His mother's cooking utensils were packed in it. He tried to shift the weight.

The other boy, who was taller and stronger, carried a blanket roll, an ax, and a bow with a handful of arrows strapped to his back. He said, "I'm tired of carrying these things, too. But we had to bring everything we own, to set up a new village here in Florida."

The boys wore long-sleeved shirts of calico in bright patterns and rawhide belts at the waist. The shirts came to their knees.

"Ouch!" said Little Fox suddenly. "I've stepped on a thorn."

He began to hop on one bare foot. Among southern Indians, men wore moccasins but women and children always went barefoot.

"Sit down here and take the thorn out," the other boy said. He pulled his friend out of line, and the two boys sat down on the warm sand. While Little Fox tried to pull out the thorn, the other boy sat cross-legged and watched the Indians go past him.

A mother walked by, carrying a sleepy baby on her back. The baby's little head nodded at each step. Next came two girls, side by side, each holding one end of a strong stick. Brass pots hung by their handles from the stick. The pots clanked together as the girls walked.

After them came two women, and they stopped. The younger woman was the boy's mother, and the older his grandmother. "Chickadee, step into line," said his mother.

"Little Fox and I won't get lost," he promised. He did wish his mother wouldn't call him by that childish name, Chickadee. It was the name of a small bird.

He longed to be given his man's name, something bold and brave that would belong to him all his life. But he was not yet old enough to have his grown-up name.

As the two women walked on, a girl's voice asked, "Have you hurt your foot?" The boys looked up to see Fat Squirrel, a pretty child with shining black hair that hung loose to her shoulders. She was holding her younger sister, Star, by the hand.

The boys smiled at the tiny child. Her brown eyes stared at them over a roasted chicken leg that she was eating. Both girls wore short skirts and brightly-colored calico capes that came down to the waist. They wore several strings of beads around their necks.

When Fat Squirrel saw the thorn, she said, "I'll take it out with my needle." To her sister she said, "Keep walking on, Star."

Fat Squirrel knelt down and opened the

leather pouch that was fastened around her waist. In it she had dried meat, a knife, wooden spoons, her sister's rag doll, and the needle. She quickly pried the thorn from Little Fox's heel. Then all three children jumped to their feet and began walking ahead once more in the long line of Indians.

Fat Squirrel sighed and she said, "I am so tired of traveling. I wonder if we will ever go back home to Georgia."

"No, never!" said Chickadee. "This will be our home forever. We will never go back because the chiefs are angry."

"Angry? What about?"

"About the war that just ended, and the peace treaty with the white men. In the treaty, the Indians had to give up hunting lands." Chickadee was talking about the War of 1812.

Fat Squirrel asked, "Why did the Creek Indians—our tribe—why did we fight in that war anyway? What do we care about any old war between the Americans and the British?"

The older boy explained, "We don't care at all what they fight about. But we do care about our own hunting grounds. We wanted to keep the Americans from cutting down more forests. We wanted to keep them from building more towns and more farms on our land."

He went on gloomily, "We fought on the British side, but the Americans won the war. So we have left the United States forever to settle here in Florida. The country of Spain owns Florida."

"I wish," said Fat Squirrel, "that white men would live at peace with Indians. But they don't seem to understand us."

Chickadee scuffed his toes through a drift of pine needles. Frowning, he said, "Indians like to be free. We want to travel freely through the forest. We want to be free to move our

16

villages from one spot to another whenever we like. We need lots of space."

Little Fox added, "That's what makes the chiefs angry. Hunting lands have belonged to us ever since we first walked here. But the white men came in their big ships. After that nothing was ever the same for us."

Chickadee said hotly, "They cut down our trees to make farms. They built roads. They pushed farther into our country."

"Never mind," said Fat Squirrel peaceably. "Now we are far, far away from the Americans. The soldiers will never bother us here."

"If they try to push us out of Florida," Chickadee said fiercely, "we will fight! The white men have pushed us farther and farther out of our hunting grounds. We will not allow them to push any more."

For a long time the three children had been talking as they walked along near the end of the file of Indians. Now they looked up in surprise as a woman came hurrying toward them. It was Fat Squirrel's mother.

"Where is your sister?" she asked sharply.

"Star? Why, she is somewhere ahead of us," said Fat Squirrel.

"No, she is not ahead of you." The mother hurried on, still searching for little Star. Now all the Indians stopped walking. Everyone looked worried. Each one tried to remember when he had seen Star last. Men on horseback galloped in every direction to try to find her.

Fat Squirrel began to cry. "This is my fault. I didn't take good care of her."

"She'll be all right. Somebody will find her," Little Fox said.

"Why don't we find her?" asked the other boy. "Maybe she wandered away while Fat Squirrel was taking that thorn out of your foot."

"That's true," Little Fox said eagerly. "Do

18

you think we could go back and find the place where we sat down?"

"Yes, I do," Chickadee said. "We will go back to that spot and look for her trail."

No one noticed the two boys slipping away. They hurried through the pine trees. It was easy to follow the path they had taken. Many feet had hollowed the sandy ground.

At last Chickadee said, "There's the place where we sat down." He pointed ahead. "I remember those two trees growing close together and that squirrel's nest high in one tree."

The boys ran forward. "If Star wandered away while we sat here," Little Fox asked, "where would she have gone?"

"Look! I see footprints on the ground. They are very small, small enough to be Star's."

The boys followed the wandering trail of footprints. It led to a shady place where thick grapevines hung down from trees.

"I think she took a nap here. See where the leaves are flattened on the ground?"

Farther ahead, Chickadee's sharp eyes saw a spot of color. He ran toward it. "Beads!" he shouted. "She broke a string of beads."

The boys went on, looking carefully all around for another sign of Star.

"Stop," Chickadee whispered sharply. "Do you hear something?"

The boys froze in place. They listened intently. "No!" they heard a small voice say in the distance. "Go away!"

"That's Star!" The boys plunged ahead, running as fast as they could toward the sound. "Star!" they shouted. "Where are you?"

A little wailing voice answered and they raced on. Suddenly Chickadee stopped short and he flung out one arm to stop Little Fox. "Wildcat," he whispered.

There was Star, walking backward step by

20

step. And there was a large gray cat, prowling toward her step by step. Its golden eyes were fixed on a piece of meat the child held. She had never finished eating that leg of chicken! The powerful muscles of the wildcat's shoulders tightened as it drew together for a spring.

"Stop!" Chickadee shouted. His voice was so loud and shrill that Little Fox, Star, and the wildcat all jumped. The cat sank flat on the ground and his head turned quickly toward the boys. As he stared at them his mouth opened in a slow, silent snarl. His head lashed back and forth angrily.

"Run with Star!" Chickadee shouted to Little Fox. As the younger boy ran toward the child, Chickadee whipped the bow from his back. He fitted an arrow to it. He took quick aim and the arrow sped toward the wildcat. But just as he fired, the cat sprang toward Star. The arrow missed by a foot.

21

Chickadee snatched another arrow and ran to stand between the animal and the other two children. "Run!" he thundered. "Run!" He heard their scrambling feet behind him. He heard Star's frightened cry.

Now the cat turned its angry attention on this loud-voiced enemy. It drew its strong body together for a leap. Chickadee pulled back his bowstring. He aimed with care and waited.

The wildcat sprang. The boy saw the claws on those outstretched forefeet. He saw lips curled back from sharp teeth. He fired his arrow, then threw himself to the ground. He was just in time. The heavy body sailed past him. It swiped his shoulder with one paw.

What was that noise? He heard the pound of horses' hoofs. He heard men's voices. Then he saw three Indians racing toward him, bent low over their horses' necks. One man pulled his horse to a halt. He raised his rifle, took quick

aim at the wildcat, and fired. The cat rolled over and over on the ground and was still.

Chickadee stood up. He turned and looked at the wildcat. He felt rather shaky. "Is Star all right?" he asked, and he rubbed his shoulder where it was scratched.

"Here she is," Little Fox called. He led Star by the hand. She was crying now, and she still clutched that piece of chicken that the wildcat had wanted.

"That great voice of yours saved you," one of the Indians said to Chickadee. He was laughing as he swung down from his horse. "You should be named The One Who Shouts Loud."

This warrior was Mad Possum. Like the other men, he wore buckskin trousers and tight leggings. All wore brightly colored calico shirts that hung halfway to their knees. Gay shawls were wound around their heads like turbans.

"When you are older," Mad Possum said,

24

"you can sing in the tribe's drinking ceremony, because your voice is so loud."

"Then you can be called Osceola," Little Fox said, "because you sing while you serve the Black Drink."

Asi is the Creek Indians' word for Black Drink, and *Yaholo* means Singer.

Mad Possum placed Star in front of him on the horse. "Let us join the others."

As the group went to join the band of Indians, Chickadee said to himself, "I will never allow anyone to call me a small bird again! Now I will have a man's name. I will be Osceola!"

The Ball Game

IT WAS TIME to camp for the night. The Indians chose a sandy space near the edge of a lake. Palmetto, live oak and orange trees grew thickly around it. Men fed and watered the ponies and dragged heavy logs to make fires. Women unpacked their cooking utensils.

"Bring a kettle of water," one mother told her daughter. "Help me gather dry sticks to start the fire," a child said to another. Even the young children had tasks.

Osceola and Little Fox were making beds. They gathered armfuls of palmetto leaves and laid them on the ground. Later, each person would roll up in blankets and lie down to sleep on a bed of leaves.

"What are the men talking about?" Osceola whispered. The boys laid down their leaves and strolled close to a group of warriors.

The leader of the band was an old man, Osceola's great-uncle. He wore a handful of white heron feathers in his blue turban. The feathers nodded gracefully as he moved his head.

"This will be a good spot for a town," the old chief said to the other warriors. "The trees are thick. We can build our village so deep in the forest that it will be hidden."

"There is plenty of game in the woods and there are fish in the lake," another man said.

"Mad Possum knows this country. He says there are other Seminole towns nearby."

"Good. We will settle here for a time."

The boys walked away and Little Fox asked, "Are Seminoles a strange tribe?"

"No," said Osceola. "Seminole is the name used for all the Indians in Florida. My great-uncle told me. Very few people are left of the ancient tribes that once lived here. For many years the country has been filling up with bands from farther north."

"Like us, coming down from Georgia."

"Yes. That's what the word Seminole means, runaway. It means people who refuse to be fenced in. It means free people."

"Then it is a good name for us!"

"Yes, it is," said Osceola. "Come, let's help to build the 'red wheels.'" They ran to help the young men drag in logs for the fires.

All through the camp, fires were being built in the same way. Logs were laid on the ground like the spokes of a wheel. All the ends touched at the center. Small sticks and dry leaves were heaped at the center, and the fire was started there. As the dry pine logs burned, they would

be pushed farther in, and would look some-
what like the spokes of a red wheel.

The boys ran to help carry logs, but they
ran for fun, not because there was any hurry.
Nobody in the Indian village hurried. No one
scolded the children. Old men sat playing
with the babies. Women talked together as .
they cooked. They were boiling stews of hom-
iny grits, sweet potatoes, and meat. Dried fish
simmered in kettles. Pans of biscuits cooked
over the embers.

"The food is ready," Osceola's grandmother
said in her high, sweet voice. "Help us carry
it to the men."

The grandmother was called Early Moon.
She was small and quick-moving, and when she
smiled one could see that she had no teeth.

The two boys picked up the handle of the
heavy kettle. They protected their hands from
heat with pads of leaves.

Osceola was proud to be the one to serve the leader of the band, his great-uncle. The old chief smiled at the boys as he dipped his long-handled spoon into the kettle of stew. The spoon, big as a cup, was carved from wood.

Other children and mothers were busy serving too. The men sat on the ground or on logs at one end of the camp. Many of them were wrapped in blankets, for the evening was chilly.

"Throw some damp leaves on the fire," one of them said. "We need heavy smoke to chase away the mosquitoes."

He slapped one cheek and then the other cheek as insects bit him, and everyone laughed. Several girls ran to gather armfuls of green leaves to make the fires smoke.

When the men had finished eating, the women and children carried the food to the other side of the camp, and they had their meal. Women and children never ate with the men.

"Let's have a ball game," Osceola shouted, jumping up. "Who wants to play?"

"I do!" Little Fox wiped grease from his mouth with the back of his hand and jumped up, too.

"That tree can be the goalpost." Osceola pointed to a tall pine sapling that stood alone. "There is plenty of space around it for the game. Who has a ball?"

Boys and girls came running, all eager to play. "Here is a ball." Fat Squirrel tossed it to Osceola. It was about the size of a golf ball, but lighter. It was made of deerskin and stuffed with deer hair.

Fat Squirrel and the other girls were dressed just like their mothers in short skirts and brightly-colored calico capes that came to the waist. Most of them wore several strands of beads around their necks. Their shining black hair fell loose to their shoulders.

"Where is my ball stick?" Osceola asked his mother. He began to rummage among the family's things, which lay in a small pile.

"I am not sure we brought it with us. Just this once, couldn't you play without a racket?" asked his mother. Her name was Gray Dove, and the name suited her. She was a quiet, soft-voiced woman with gentle eyes.

Osceola looked at her in astonishment. "Play like a girl?" he exclaimed. "What would the other boys think of me!"

In a minute he found the racket, concealed in the folds of a blanket. It was carved from laurel wood, and one end was bent into an "O" shape. Leather thongs were crossed in this circle, making a cup for catching a ball.

One of the men was chopping away the lower branches of the goalpost tree. He left just a cluster of branches at the top, which looked much like a big feather duster.

"Here's the ball, Mad Possum," Osceloa called. He tossed it to the young warrior. "This way, this way," he shouted, and he led half of the players, in a jumble of laughing and jumping children, to one side of the goalpost. The other half of the players moved back to the opposite side of the field.

Mad Possum stood at the center of the field. He tossed the ball high in the air to start the game. When it came down, everyone scrambled to hit it. Each team tried to score a point by making the ball hit the tree.

Boys swung at it with their ball sticks. Girls were allowed to use their hands. The ball bounced back and forth. Sometimes it was high in the air, sometimes it rolled on the ground.

"I made a point!" someone shouted.

One of the young braves pushed among the players. He made a charcoal line on the side of the tree to show a point scored.

Someone threw the ball, and the game was on again. Everyone was laughing. A boy's ball stick hit someone in the head, but he didn't look around to see who was hurt. A girl stumbled to her knees on the rough ground and skinned her hands, but she went on playing. Children bumped together, they tripped over each other, and they often fell.

"Another point for our side!" It was Osceola's shrill voice rising above the clamor.

On the sidelines, men and women and the youngest children sat watching. They were laughing and cheering too. A three-year-old jumped up and down, shouting and clapping her hands in excitement.

Suddenly Osceola stopped playing. The ball flashed past his head and he didn't even notice it. He was staring at four strangers on horseback. They were lined up in the shadows of the trees, watching the ball game.

Strangers Visit the Camp

ONE BY ONE other players saw what Osceola was staring at. They too forgot the game and stood still. The ball fell to the ground, rolled a few inches, and stopped.

One minute the Seminole camp was noisy, rollicking, full of laughter and running. The next minute all was still. Young warriors lying on the ground or leaning against tree trunks stood up with dignity. The old men stopped smiling. Their faces became expressionless.

Two white men dismounted from their horses. Their clothes were dusty and rumpled from travel. Osceola saw that a third rider was a woman on a sidesaddle. The fourth was a boy who looked younger than himself.

The old chief had been sitting on a log with several other men. They all stood up and faced the newcomers without smiling.

One of the white men took off his tall hat and called out a greeting as he walked forward. He held out one hand in a friendly way. His voice was loud and cheerful, but Osceola could not understand the words. The man was speaking English, and few Indians knew the language.

One of the Negroes who belonged to the band went to stand behind Osceola's great-uncle. This was Isaac, who had once been a slave on a Georgia plantation. Now he lived as a free man. He was called the chief's sense-bearer because he was a close friend and advisor. Of course he spoke English easily.

"He gives you his greetings," Isaac told the old chief. "He says he comes in peace."

When he heard this, the old man stepped toward his visitors. Osceola was proud to see how stately the chief looked.

"You are welcome," he said in his own language. Stretching out his hands, he clasped the other man's arms. The white man knew this was the Indian way of shaking hands. He clasped the chief's arms. He smiled and nodded, and waved one hand toward the other stranger. He spoke very fast in his strange language.

Isaac translated. "His name is George Irving and he has a plantation nearby. His friend is named Sims, and he also is a planter."

Now six or seven of the warriors came forward. They gripped the arms of Irving and Sims, one after the other. They were showing good manners, but they did not smile or relax. They were waiting to see just how friendly these two men would prove to be.

"Tell them to sit down and we will talk," the

old chief said. He waved with one hand toward the seat of honor, where blankets were laid across a log. The two men sat down and the chief sat beside them. Other Indians sank to the ground in a circle, facing them.

Osceola saw his grandmother go to her kettle beside a fire. He ran to her side. "Let me carry some of the food to them," he said.

"Be careful not to spill any," she whispered. She spooned a serving of stew into a bowl carved from cypress wood. Osceola took it in both hands and walked carefully toward the guests. No one was talking now. It would not be polite to talk until the callers had eaten.

He looked quickly into the two men's faces. Sims had a thin face with pinched-in lips. He looked gloomy and cross. Osceola stepped past him and handed the bowl to the other one, Mr. Irving. This man looked up smiling and took it in his hands with some strange words that

Osceola knew must be his way of expressing thanks. Then Mr. Irving looked here and there as if he didn't know just what to do next.

Isaac said in a low voice, "He doesn't know how to eat without a fork." Turning to the men, he made motions with his hands, as if he were picking up bits of meat and potatoes and putting them into his mouth.

Mr. Irving laughed good-naturedly. He fished bits of food from the bowl and ate them. He nodded and smiled as if he were saying that the food was good.

Osceola stepped back. His grandmother had given Mr. Sims a bowl of stew, and the white man was holding it. He dipped in his fingers as if he were not hungry, or as if he didn't like the Indian way of eating.

"I wish I could sit down with the men and listen to the talk," Osceola thought.

Everyone was quiet. Mothers held their small

children to keep them still. Osceola, who was a well brought up Indian boy, went to sit down near his mother. Young men who were not important enough to be in the talking group stood with arms folded and looked far away.

Girls went quietly about their tasks. They wiped spoons clean with leaves, or pushed logs farther into the fire. People acted as if they hardly knew that strangers were in camp, but really everyone was listening hard.

A horse pawed the earth impatiently. Osceola saw the woman on the sidesaddle lean down and hand two empty wooden dishes to Fat Squirrel. He was glad that the mother and the child had been given food, too.

"Mad Possum has seen them before," someone whispered to Osceola. "They are Mr. Irving's wife and son."

Osceola's attention went back to the men's talk. He listened closely.

"Mr. Irving says he hopes we have good hunting," Isaac was saying. "He says Florida is a big place. There is room for the red man and the white man. We can all live in peace."

"Give him our thanks," the old chief told Isaac. "Ask him where his plantation is. We will agree not to hunt on his land."

Isaac repeated this in English. Then he said, "His plantation lies ten miles to the east. He hopes you will be his guest some day."

Now the other man muttered to Mr. Irving. His voice sounded angry.

Isaac said, "The angry one says Mr. Irving is a fool to be a friend to Indians. He says we will take the scalps of the Irving family whenever we feel like it."

The old chief's voice sounded angry in its turn. "Tell him that Indians do not attack farms unless our towns are attacked first," he told Isaac.

After a little more talk, Isaac reported, "Mr. Sims says that Indian towns are never attacked unless the Indians have first made war." He shook his head sadly. "This is always the way. Each side claims that the other side made trouble first."

All the men stood up now. Mr. Irving drew a big silk handkerchief, brightly patterned in green and white, from his pocket. He folded it and held it out to the chief with a bow.

The old warrior accepted it. He looked pleased, and in return handed the white heron feathers from his turban to Mr. Irving.

Osceola was watching. He knew that an Indian always presented a gift in return for one given to him. He was glad that his great-uncle had something so nice to give this man.

The Indians escorted their callers back to the horses. In a few minutes the white people rode away into the woods.

The Deer Hunt

IT WAS three days later. Osceola blinked his eyes open. He was looking straight up into the ceiling of his house, which Seminoles call a "chickee." The roof was made from layers of bark and palmetto leaves, and logs were laid on top to keep the leaves from blowing away. The roof sloped down steeply on two sides.

Osceola rolled over onto his hands and knees and shook off his blanket. He had on his daytime clothes, for no Indian bothered to wear a nightgown. His mother was lying on one side of him and his grandmother, snoring slightly, on the other side. They were still asleep.

45

Osceola felt excited and happy, but for a minute he couldn't think why. "I remember now," he said to himself. "Mad Possum promised to take me hunting today."

He stood up and rolled his blanket into a neat package. "I would tuck it into the rafters," he thought, "but I am not tall enough."

Of course the house had no furniture. No beds, no chairs, no chests of drawers. Everything the family owned was wrapped in bundles and stored in the rafters. There it was safe from rain and out of people's way.

The boy tiptoed across the rough wooden floor and dropped from the edge of it to the ground. The house stood up on poles about three feet above the ground. It had no walls.

He was thinking, "The nights will soon be colder. Then we will have to hang skins across the sides of the house to keep us warm."

He walked softly to his mother's fire. Only

a small curl of grey smoke rose lazily from it. Logs had burned away so that only their charred ends lay in a circle like a burnt wheel. He pushed them through soft ashes until all their tips were together. He sprinkled a handful of pine chips over the embers at the center and blew on them to make them catch fire.

A hand touched his shoulder and he looked up. Mad Possum stood there grinning at him. The young man was tall and slender, and he was always full of fun. He stood knotting his turban firmly around his head.

"Let us go," he whispered. "It will soon be sunrise."

"But we haven't had breakfast."

"The hunter who waits for breakfast may miss the game. Come."

Osceola looked hungrily toward his mother's kettle. But Mad Possum was already walking silently across the clearing. He picked up his rifle from the floor of his own hut as he passed. He slung a powder horn on a long strap across one shoulder and tied a leather pouch containing shot around his waist. Indian clothes had no pockets, so whatever a person carried he put into a bag, or pouch.

Osceola picked up his bow and arrows and followed the hunter. A sleepy, brown-faced girl was stepping down from her house, and she smiled at Osceola. Nearby, Fat Squirrel was quietly placing kindling on a fire. But most people still lay fast asleep in their houses.

Osceola walked behind Mad Possum. They left the village and entered a thick forest. They moved quietly, looking carefully from side to side. They dodged the tatters of Spanish moss that hung down and brushed their faces.

Osceola shivered in the chilly air. A flock of goldfinches swooped through a clearing. He heard their little twittering voices.

"Watch," Mad Possum whispered. The two Indians stopped at the edge of a bank to look down into a bowl-shaped hollow. There, among the tall, coarse grasses, a hundred or more birds had taken shelter for the night. They were just waking up.

"There go the terns," Osceola murmured. The trim little white birds with shining black caps ruffled their feathers. One by one they rose in the air and flew off swiftly.

The boy grinned to see a white ibis open his curved, red beak wide. "As if he is yawning," Osceola thought. A long-legged stilt waded a few steps in the water, looking for fish. Whooping cranes sprang into the air. Their thin legs stretched out behind them as they flew. Wood ibis lifted their heavy bodies and flew away.

Osceola drew his bow to aim at a sleepy wood ibis stalking among the reeds. Ibis made good eating. But he dropped his hands. It was early in the day. He might find bigger game. In a few minutes, all the birds had flown away.

The hunters walked on. The sun came up and the boy began to feel warmer. He saw rabbits and a raccoon and once, near a creek, he saw a pair of otter. But Mad Possum was hoping for something larger today.

Osceola said to himself, "I wish we had brought some food. I feel very hungry. But if Mad Possum can go on and on without eating, then so can I."

Now they walked out of the woods. They were in a wide, sunny meadow. Osceola's bare legs were wet and chilled from brushing through tall grass. It was still soaked with dew.

Mad Possum pointed with his rifle.

"Deer feeding," Osceola whispered.

Two brown deer were moving into the far side of the meadow. They were a quarter of a mile away. They took a few steps, then bent their heads to nibble the grass. Next a head would lift quickly and turn left and right. Then, satisfied that they were safe, the deer would bend their necks again to eat. They walked a few steps nearer. Their short tails jerked as they walked.

"The wind is from them to us," Osceola thought. "They will not catch our scent. We will not alarm them if we walk quietly."

They moved carefully. When both brown animals' heads were buried in the grass, the hunters crept forward. A deer would lift its head. Instantly the Indians stood very still.

"Mad Possum always stands with his side to the deer," Osceola noticed. "He doesn't move a muscle when the deer look up. They must think we are tree trunks."

Step by step they drew closer to the deer. Osceola never took his eyes from them.

"I can tell something!" he thought. "I can

tell by the way a deer moves his shoulders when he is just about to lift his head."

The two hunters both froze the second before a deer looked up. Finally they had stolen close enough so that they were within shooting range. Mad Possum lifted his rifle and took careful aim. A shot rang out.

One deer jumped and then fell forward to the ground. The other one looked up straight at the hunters. Then he turned and bounded out of the meadow and into the safety of the trees. He seemed to leap as lightly as a bit of milkweed fluff.

"You got it with one shot!" Osceola shouted. He began to run toward the game. He felt as though he jumped as lightly as the deer.

Mad Possum was grinning happily as he came up to inspect the deer, a young buck.

"This will feed many families tonight," he said. "Help me tie his legs together."

Osceola knew how animals were carried. He helped fasten the deer's front legs to Mad Possum's shoulders. With strips of rawhide he tied the middle of the animal to Mad Possum's waist. Then he tied the hind legs together.

"It makes a heavy load," Mad Possum said. "I know a short-cut back to the town."

Osceola followed. He carried an arrow ready to fire if he saw a bird or small animal.

When they had walked for a long time, Mad Possum said, "We are approaching a lake where many alligators live."

The lake was soon in view and Osceola said, "I don't see any alligators now. No doubt they are spending the day asleep on the bottom of the lake."

Mad Possum looked over one shoulder with his teasing grin. "I'll show you an alligator," he said. He drew a deep breath and suddenly gave a bellowing roar. Osceola jumped. It sounded exactly like an alligator, but it was really Mad Possum imitating its roar.

"Look there!" Osceola pointed. "An alligator is coming up to talk to you."

At the edge of the lake, water heaved and bubbled. Then the long, dark head of a large alligator broke into the air. Its little eyes seemed to stare at the Indians. Moving quickly on its short legs, it slid half its body onto the shore. It opened its great mouth and roared loudly.

"That's more noise than you can make!" Osceola cried delightedly. He was not afraid of the alligator, knowing that it was not likely to attack in daylight.

The creature turned its head this way and that, looking for the alligator that it thought had called out. It gave one more bellow. Then it curved its long, wet body and slid back under the water and disappeared.

"Sometimes I can make half a dozen of them

come up to answer me," Mad Possum boasted. He swung the deer into a more comfortable position on his back and started to walk forward. He didn't look where he was going.

"A rattlesnake!" shouted Osceola.

Mad Possum jumped to one side. He was too late. He had nearly stepped on a coiled rattler. Osceola heard the snake's high-pitched rattle, like the buzz of grasshoppers. The snake opened its mouth wide and struck at Mad Possum's leg. Its two curved fangs struck through the thin leather of the leggings.

Mad Possum jerked away. The snake wavered, its head high in the air. Then it turned and glided out of sight among some low bushes.

"Quick," said Mad Possum. "Untie the deer so I can sit down. The poison is under my skin."

Osceola Runs
for Help

Osceola untied the rawhide. The deer slid to the ground. Mad Possum sat down and rolled one legging to his ankle. Osceola bent over the wound and looked at it closely.

"I see two marks where the fangs sank in," he said. "Here, at the back of your calf."

"Cut an 'X' over each spot."

"I can suck out the poison," Osceola said. "I saw my grandmother do it once when a water moccasin bit one of the babies."

Already the skin was turning purple where the fangs had struck. Osceola took the sharp hunting knife Mad Possum drew from his belt.

He made the small cuts. Then he bent down and quickly drew fluid from the wounds. He reached for the thong that had bound the deer to Mad Possum's shoulders. He tied the leather strip snugly around the leg, above the wounds.

"You will be all right," Osceola said. "I will run to the town to get help for you."

"I feel very dizzy," Mad Possum said. He lay back flat on the ground.

"You will need a drink." Osceola jumped up and seized a handful of broad leaves from a tree. He twisted one into the shape of a cup but it tore. He shaped another cup, but when he dipped it into the lake, water leaked from it. The third leaf made a fairly good cup. Mad Possum sat up on one elbow and drank the cool water gladly.

Osceola was alarmed to see that the leg was already more swollen. Once more he bent down and extracted fluid from the cuts.

"Now I will go for help," he said. "Which way is the town?"

"That way," said Mad Possum faintly. But his eyes were closed and his hands were limp on the ground. He did not point in any direction.

Osceola turned around in a complete circle. Now he was really frightened.

"If I run in the wrong direction," he thought, "I will go farther from help every minute. Mad Possum might die here while I am lost in strange country."

Then he drew himself up stiffly. "He is my best friend among the grown warriors," he thought. "I will have to be clever enough to do the right thing. I know I can't go that way— into the lake. I don't want to go there—that is the way we came here. Which way do I feel is the right direction?"

He made himself relax. He looked thoughtfully all around. He tried to remember exactly how he and Mad Possum had turned and turned when they wandered about in search of game.

"Most of the time the sun was on my right side," he told himself. "So when I go back I will keep it on my left side. And I do have a feeling that the village lies that way."

He pointed a steady hand toward the spot he had chosen. He set off running.

"I must not run too hard," he warned himself. "I must save my strength so I will not have to stop for a rest."

He jogged along at a steady pace. For a while he followed the edge of the lake. Then he turned left and followed a valley between two low hills. He grew very thirsty and very hot.

"But Mad Possum is thirstier than I, and by now he may be even hotter with fever." Osceola would not let himself think of his own discomfort. He bruised one heel on a stone, but he ran steadily on.

"There," he said happily. "That's the hollow where we watched the birds. Now I know where I am." It was not much farther to the Indian town. Osceola was glad to see the cooking fires of home, and to see his own friends strolling on the clean-swept street.

He saw his great-uncle in the chief's house talking with two other men. Osceola was so tired that he was stumbling. He ran jerkily toward the old man. He sat right down on the ground in front of the house.

"Mad Possum," he gulped. "Snake bite. Needs help." He was gasping for breath.

Men and women and curious children clustered around him. The boy could hardly sit up. Every muscle in his body was trembling. Someone handed him a dipper full of honey and water. He shut his eyes to enjoy the drink fully and told about the rattlesnake.

"Rest for a few minutes," said his grandmother. "Drink a little turtle soup. Then you can lead the men back to Mad Possum."

Someone wiped his streaming face with a cool, wet cloth. Someone else fanned him.

"You were a good runner, to come so far without resting," a warrior said approvingly.

Little Fox touched his shoulder and teased him by saying, "Why didn't you lift your great big voice and shout for help? We could have heard you many miles away."

Osceola's mother laughed with the others, but she said, "He had the good sense not to waste his breath on shouting."

"He always acts with good sense," Osceola heard one of the braves say.

"I am ready to go back now," the boy said. "We must not lose any time."

"Here, I will help you mount this horse," someone said. "We will all ride horses."

Osceola led the men at a fast pace. At last

they reached Mad Possum and found him in much pain. But he said cheerfully, "Osceola must have found the short-cut. When you take me back to camp, remember to take the deer, too."

"We will. Lie still and let me put this compress on your leg. The medicine man sent it."

The men built a stretcher from poles and a blanket to carry Mad Possum to his house. For several days he lay on a pile of palmetto leaves and blankets recovering from the poison.

Osceola went to visit him. "My grandmother sent you this," he said. He handed Mad Possum a little package wrapped in a cloth. It contained many dried leaves. "There is good magic in these herbs. Tie it around your neck and tomorrow smoke some of it," he said.

"Thank you," the man said, smiling up at Osceola. "And here comes the medicine man. He will make me well."

Old Shooting Star climbed stiffly into the house. He carried a cup of steaming tea in one hand. In the other he had a flat tin pan and on it was another cup.

He said to Osceola, "Bring me a brand from a fire." The boy ran to obey. He hurried back with a pine stick that burned at one end.

Shooting Star took it from him. His old hand trembled a little, but he thrust the burning end into the cup that held crushed leaves. Osceola had no idea what kind of leaves they were. Medicine men did not tell their secrets. Soon the leaves began to smoulder.

Shooting Star carried the cup slowly all around the house, from one corner to another. One by one villagers gathered until they formed a square around the house. All their faces were very serious. They believed that Shooting Star could make the sick man well.

The medicine man sang in his cracked old voice. No one knew what the words were. The tune was slow and monotonous, with tones that glided down the scale, and then began again at a high pitch.

Osceola had slipped down from the house and was standing beside his mother. "What is he doing to the tea?" he whispered to her.

Shooting Star put down the smoking leaves. He blew into the cup of tea through a cattail reed. The liquid foamed and bubbled.

"He is blowing prayers into it," Gray Dove said in a low voice.

"Now—Mad Possum is drinking the prayers," Osceola murmured. Shooting Star also drank part of the tea. An Indian doctor always took the same medicine he gave his patients. This proved that he had faith in it. Shooting Star finished his treatment and climbed down from the house.

Osceola said to his mother, "I remembered to throw a piece of Mad Possum's deer meat into the fire the day he was poisoned. That will bring him good luck too."

As he went quietly away with the other Indians, Osceola was thinking, "Who knows which medicine will cure him? But I am glad I ran back to camp in time to get help for him."

Mr. Sims Comes Again

"WHAT A NICE doll house this will be," Fat Squirrel said.

Osceola sat cross-legged on the ground. He was building a doll's chickee for Fat Squirrel and two other little girls.

"It's just like the house you live in, only smaller," he said.

It was a still, sunny day in early June. All through the calm, tidy village, people were sitting at rest or were quietly busy. Gray Dove was talking with a group of other women as they scraped animal skins or sewed moccasins.

Three girls sat at the edge of a house and

swung their bare legs above the ground. They sang a lullaby in soft voices while they wove baskets from dried grasses. Some younger children played cat's cradle with loops of string on their fingers. Babies toddled around the clean-swept yards, and their mothers watched them. In the garden beyond the village, melons and sweet potatoes were being hoed by Negro members of the band. They cared more about farming than the Seminoles did.

"Now I need some shredded leaves to make the roof," Osceola said.

"Here are the leaves. Make the roof watertight," Fat Squirrel said. "We don't want our dolls to get wet on a rainy night."

The doll she held in her arms was carved from wood. Her father had made it. Her mother had given her the scraps of red and blue calico to make its dress.

"Boys!" A young warrior named Howling

Wolf called from the edge of the clearing. "We have some work for you to do. Come!"

Osceola jumped to his feet. "I must go help the men," he said.

"We'll finish the house," Fat Squirrel said. "We can make a roof as well as a boy can."

"Come with me, Little Fox. Come along, Black Water and Turtle," Osceola called.

He and several other boys left their work or play and ran to the place where the young man waited. Because he was working hard and the day was warm, he wore no clothes except a cotton cloth draped around his hips. His brown skin shone in the sun. He was known to be a fierce fighter, but among his friends he was soft-spoken and gentle.

He smiled gravely at the boys. "We want you to set up some braces," he said. "Mad Possum and the others are bringing a fine cypress log to camp. We are going to make a boat."

"A fresh log?" Osceola asked in surprise.

"No, no. We would never build a boat from fresh wood. This tree was prepared more than a year ago. Are you boys too young to be able to count the moons? We have lived in Florida through two winters."

The boys laughed. One said, "When we came from Georgia, we brought no boats."

"Yes," Howling Wolf said. "So in the first weeks we were here, we found a good cypress tree about four feet thick and made it ready."

Little Fox said, "My father told me he helped to cut down the tree. Then it was buried in mud beside a creek and left to season."

Osceola could not boast about having a father who had helped start the boat. But he could show off his knowledge. "Wood that is well seasoned in mud will never crack or check," he said. "Here comes the log now."

Twelve men, walking slowly in step, came

70

through the trees. They balanced a thirty-foot log on their shoulders. It had only the rough shape of a boat.

"Put it down here," Osceola shouted. "We will get the braces ready for you."

The boys ran to set wedges in a shady spot under some trees to keep the log steady. They used tree trunks and rocks for braces.

"I know where there are some fine shells," Osceola said. "All of them are big strong ones with sharp edges."

He and the other boys ran to the spot at the edge of the village where bones and shells, ashes, and broken pieces of homemade pottery were dumped, out of the way.

"Mad Possum, these are all for you," Osceola called. He ran back to the boat with as many conch shells as he could carry. The warrior's snake bite had healed long ago. He was now as strong as ever.

All over the village, people put down their work. They strolled toward the boat builders. They admired the fineness of the log. Old men talked about good boats they had helped to build, long ago. Little boys planned to carve toy boats just like the big one.

While the other people from the village talked, men were building smouldering fires inside the log. It was already partly hollowed out. As the cypress burned, they scraped away the charred wood with their shells.

Osceola sat with the other boys, watching. After a long time, his eyes drifted away. Suddenly he shouted, "Look! The corn is tasseling! It is getting ripe! I can see it from here." He pointed to the garden.

Everyone looked toward the corn field. Mad Possum's face puckered into a slow grin.

"The corn tassels every year," he said teasingly. "Why are you excited now?"

Osceola laughed. "Everybody knows why, Mad Possum! When the corn is ripe, it is time for the Green Corn Dance!"

"Oh, the Green Corn Dance," Mad Possum said, as if he had never thought of it before. He dropped his shell on the ground and went to sit down beside Osceola. He wiped the sweat from his face and fanned himself with a big green leaf. "What fun we will have then," he said dreamily. "The dancing and the feasting— oho! I can hardly wait."

"No doubt the invitations will be sent out soon," the old chief said.

Suddenly Mad Possum's face lost its merry expression. He was looking over Osceola's shoulder toward the far side of the village.

"Strangers are coming," he said. "I think I recognize the man in the gray suit. He has been here before."

Osceola turned to look. Everyone else turned

too. Half a dozen grim-faced men were dismounting from horses.

"The one in front is the man Sims," Osceola said. "He was here one day long ago with Mr. Irving. We didn't like Mr. Sims."

He jumped to his feet and moved closer to his great-uncle. If there was going to be trouble, the old chief would be at the center of it. Osceola wanted to be there, too.

"I wish he had on his feather-trimmed cape," he thought. "Nobody is so handsome as my great-uncle when he wears the cape."

Since he had not expected visitors, the old chief wore his every-day shirt of wrinkled blue calico. Even so, he looked very dignified as he waited for the callers to come closer.

Mr. Sims and the men with him strode toward the group of quiet Indians under the orange trees. Mr. Sims wore a pistol in the belt of his riding breeches. The other men carried

rifles. They were dressed in rough working clothes, and Mr. Sims seemed to be their leader.

He stopped in front of the chief and nodded curtly but did not smile. His narrow face looked pinched and angry. He began to talk very fast. He snapped out his words as if he were giving orders. But of course he spoke English, and no Indian understood a word.

Isaac, the Negro sensebearer, slipped up to stand beside the chief. Isaac said in his soft voice, "The man says that a band of wild young Indians set fire to his corn crib. They stole twelve head of cattle. He has come to get his cattle back."

"They were not our warriors. We do not have his cattle," the chief said. He drew himself up tall and folded his arms over his chest. He and the planter stared coldly at each other.

Now Early Moon and several other women drew near. She carried a bowlful of honey and water for the visitors. The others had panfuls of bread, called koontie, to offer them.

But Isaac waved them away with a small motion of his hand. The women understood that the gesture meant, "No, these men are not friends." They quietly moved away again.

Isaac translated the chief's words into English. Then he told the Indians what the strangers said.

Mr. Sims said angrily, "You've killed my cattle for food! In return, I'm going to drive off those ponies of yours."

A man stepped forward quickly. "We won't do that for you. We came here to help you round up your cattle, nothing else."

"These Indians aren't to be trusted! They've burnt my corn crib——"

"I'm sorry, sir," another man said. "We're going to keep the peace if we can. The Seminoles outnumber us."

"Besides," said a third man, "maybe these aren't the guilty ones."

Mr. Sims looked furiously into the face of every young Seminole. "If I ever see one of you on my plantation," he said, "I'll come back and burn down every hut in this place."

He turned and stalked away. The other men followed him silently. All remounted their horses and rode away, looking back over their shoulders as they went. Until they were out of sight, no Indian moved or spoke.

Then the chief said angrily, "We will return attack for attack. We will not be pushed around by these men!"

The older men moved away, talking earnestly. Women went back to their work. The boat builders started to scrape again.

Osceola said to Little Fox, "I don't believe it! Nobody has stolen his cattle."

But Howling Wolf rubbed his hand along the

gunwale of the boat. "It is probably true," he said. "Hot-blooded warriors make raids on the homesteads. Then the settlers band together and attack a Seminole town."

"They want to push us into the swamp lands far to the south," another man said. "That will leave the best lands for them. They are afraid to have us living too close to them."

"They had better be afraid," Mad Possum said threateningly. "We will go to war rather than surrender any more of our country."

Osceola said to Little Fox, "Did you notice that while the strangers were here, not a single Negro was to be seen, except Isaac?"

"That's true. I wonder why they hid."

"Don't you know?" Osceola said. "Some of them are runaways. They have taken refuge with us, the free people. Here they are as free as we are. They don't want to be captured and taken back to work on the plantations."

The Green Corn Dance

OSCEOLA and four other boys strolled into the village from the garden. They had been there all morning. Their task had been to chase away blackbirds and crows by running about, whooping, and waving their arms.

"Look there." Osceola pointed. "Isaac is hanging up sticks on a tree branch. The village must have been invited to the Green Corn Dance! Quick, let's count the sticks."

All the boys ran to old Isaac. He grinned at them. "Fifteen sticks," he said. "That means fifteen days until the festival."

"Each day you'll take down one stick, won't

you?" Black Water said. "When the last one is down, it will be time for the dance."

Isaac pretended to be very severe with the boys. He said, "You boys will have much work to do, helping your families to get ready. Everybody will have to carry a supply of food to the head chief's town."

"Why? Won't there be any food there?" Black Water asked in surprise.

The others laughed at him. "Of course," Isaac said. "But there will be many, many Seminole bands gathering in for the dance. No one could feed us all. We must take corn and meat with us for the feasts."

"I'll go hunting at once!" Osceola shouted.

He raced to his house to get his bow and arrows. His grandmother was there. She was sweeping the yard smooth with a broom made of several bunches of brush, tied together.

She straightened up and pushed the loose,

white hair out of her eyes. "Wait, grandson. Stay in the village. Your mother needs your help in pounding the koontie. We must have plenty of flour to take to the Green Corn Dance."

"Pound the koontie! Me?" Osceola said in dismay. "That's a job for a girl, or for a child younger than me."

The old lady laughed. "All must help to get ready for the journey," she said.

Osceola saw his mother in a group of girls and children in the shade of the palmettos. He walked toward her with dragging steps.

"I see the pounding logs are ready," he said, looking at them gloomily.

The pounding logs were pine logs, laid flat on the ground. Three or four holes had been cut in each one. The holes were about ten inches across the top, and they were carved deep into the wood, down to a point.

"Pieces of koontie and water are already in

the holes," Gray Dove said. "Here is a stick."
She handed him a smooth pole about as long as
he was tall. He put it into one of the holes and
began beating it up and down, up and down, to
to turn the koontie into pulp.

Koontie is a plant that grows wild in the
Florida woods. Women had already gathered
the roots. They had washed and scraped them
and cut them into small pieces.

Gray Dove said, "As soon as that batch is
well pounded, pour it into this cloth and let it
strain. The starch will filter onto the deerskin
laid here on the ground."

"I know how to do it," Osceola said resign-
edly. "But I hope by next year you will know
I am too old for this kind of work. I'll strain
the koontie and then dry it on palmetto leaves.
Finally it will be a pale yellow flour. But tell
me why the bread is that bright orange color
after it is baked."

"I don't know why," his mother said, smiling. "I do know you must spend many days pounding, straining, and drying the koontie for me."

Osceola pounded koontie until his arms ached. But he was not the only one with special tasks. Fat Squirrel and the other girls worked at laundry, because everyone must go to the dance with clean clothes. They did the washing by spreading garments on rocks beside a stream and pounding them with blocks of wood until all the dirt was beaten and rinsed away.

The men went hunting every day. Mothers worked many hours preparing great bags and baskets for carrying supplies.

Every day the boys and girls counted Isaac's sticks. Every day he took one down. When only five sticks remained, he said, "Tomorrow we will go. That will give us several days on the trail. A large band like this, with so many babies and small children, cannot travel fast."

The journey itself was like a holiday. There was no need to go quietly because no one was hunting. There were no enemies to fear. Little children romped along the path. Sometimes they rode on their fathers' backs. Boys fanned out in chattering, whooping groups.

They wound through forests. They passed many, many lakes. They walked around the swampy places. At night they camped under trees, and slept on the ground.

They reached the head chief's village late on the third afternoon. Even before they could see the town, they heard its noise.

Hundreds of voices talking at once made a sound like small waves breaking over rocks. It was a pleasant sound with laughter in it. The closer they came to the town, the louder the noise was.

As last the travelers rounded the last turn in the trail. The village lay in full sight.

"What a big town!" Osceola said. "There are so many people!"

The town was spread over a very broad clearing. It was surrounded by palmetto trees. Crowds of men stood talking together or strolling about. Women were busy at cooking fires. They gossiped together as they worked. Children darted in and out of the groups. Boys and girls played a lively ball game. A big crowd watched and cheered them.

"We are not the first band to arrive," Gray Dove said. "See the new houses built so that some visitors can sleep under shelter."

Osceola saw that she was looking eagerly into the swarms of women. She was hunting for the faces of old friends and relatives.

"Everyone is dressed in his best clothes," Little Fox whispered to Osceola.

The girls' capes were of the brightest colors. So were the men's shirts and turbans. Afternoon sun twinkled on beads, on silver ornaments, and on shell-trimmed garments. Where men stood talking together, there was a lovely, restless waving of feathers on their heads.

Everyone was gay, but no one was boisterous. There was much quiet laughter. Women stayed modestly at one end of the village. The hum of their voices rose and fell like soft music.

Osceola and his friends moved around in an excited little pack.

"It's almost dark," Little Fox said. "The best fun is after dark."

"I know where the council square is," Black Water boasted. "The place where all the dances and talks are held."

Osceola said, "As soon as we have eaten, let's go at once to the council square."

It was very dark when the boys had eaten all they wanted. They joined a steady stream of Indians walking from the town to the dancing place. They followed a winding path through the woods. It was so dark that Osceola could see almost nothing. But ahead of him and behind him he heard the soft pad of footsteps and the rustle of garments.

"How dark it is," he murmured. Just then he stumbled over a root and nearly fell.

"Keep on the path and walk slowly," said a voice behind him. "We are less likely to be hit by a snake if we do not hurry."

"Aha!" Osceola said to himself. "We have almost reached the council square. I can see light ahead."

The square was indeed light. At the center a great fire sent flames shooting straight toward the sky. Hundreds of men and boys were milling about. Osceola looked all around and found that he was separated from his friends. He sat down on the ground and was squeezed by a dense pack of people.

All the men and boys were facing the fire in a great circle. There were no women or girls to be seen. Osceola knew that they were not allowed on the square except when they were dancing. Light flickered over smiling faces, for everyone was in high spirits.

A hum of talk filled the air. Behind the Indians, a ring of tall trees was dimly lighted. Deeper in the forest, all was black.

"I helped to build the council house," said someone behind Osceola. He looked around into the face of an older boy, about fifteen years old. He was a slim and handsome youth with a proud, serious face.

"My name is Panther," he said. "In a few years I will be old enough to sit there with the chiefs and warriors."

By now nearly everyone was sitting down. Osceola peered this way and that over the heads of feathered, turbaned, shawled, and silver-trimmed men. Then he saw the council house. It was a long building with a thatch roof and open sides. Many men sat there, cross-legged on the floor.

"I see my great-uncle," Osceola said, "and Howling Wolf and Mad Possum." He explained, "They are warriors from my village."

"Great fighters, I have no doubt," Panther said politely. "Look—the dancing is about to start. There's the leader." Panther pointed to him. "He is the man carrying a coconut shell rattle in his hand."

The dance track was ten feet wide and it made a circle around the fire. It was already beaten hard by stamping feet.

The leader started the dance. Men and women now surged onto the dance floor in couples and walked the circle after him, keeping step. He sang a chanting, melancholy song. Osceloa swayed, keeping time to the rattle.

Light from the red wheel flickered on all the watchers. Dancers on the far side of the fire moved in brilliant light. Those on the near side were outlined black and clear against the blaze. The song ended and the leader shook his coconut rattle. Osceola opened his mouth and with all the others he shouted, "Ho, ho, ho!"

Next the couples faced each other, still in their big circle. Each one took his partner by the shoulders and they swayed from side to side.

"It's exactly like an alligator, curled in a ring and heaving his body!" Osceola said.

An old man behind him leaned forward. "The dance is supposed to look like an alligator," he said. "This is the alligator dance. Alligators made it up long ago, when all the animals talked like people."

Osceola looked up into a thin and wrinkled face. He had heard the story many times, but he nodded politely.

"Some day," the old man went on, "when all the people are dead, the animals will again talk in words." His voice was drowned out by another shout of "Ho, ho, ho!" and the rattle of the coconut shell.

"I like this next dance, the stamping one," Osceola said to Panther. The alligator dance was finished. Men who had taken part in it took seats in the audience. The women went back to their more distant place under the trees. A new group of dancers was forming a ring around the blazing fire.

"*Thump—thump—thump,*" went a singer's hand on his cypress drum. He sat at the edge of the dancing circle. He raised his voice in a sad song. Men and women moved around the circle, stamping their feet. First the men stamped, then the women.

The women wore a pair of turtle shells tied to each knee. There were tiny pebbles inside the shells. When they stamped their feet in time, all the rattles jangled in a glorious, exciting rhythm.

"That one's my mother," Osceola said to Panther. "That one in the skirt trimmed with little shells."

He watched Gray Dove proudly. Her face was usually sweet and serious, but now it was merry and smiling. He could see that she loved taking part in the dance.

Each time the singer finished, the dancers sang the chorus. Then there was more stamping, and more of that jingling of the rattles. It filled the whole forest with its thrilling sound. Osceola watched entranced.

When the dance ended, Gray Dove glided away from the dance circle with the other women. She walked past Osceola and gave him a wink and a smile. She walked so cleverly that the rattles didn't make a sound!

Seminole Court Day

FOR SEVERAL DAYS the Seminoles feasted and danced. Osceola and his friends of course danced too. Even the youngest children did. Learning the dances was considered an important part of their education.

Every afternoon until dusk the children played their ball game.

Then came the most important day of the Green Corn Dance. It was known as Court Day.

Osceola woke up when the east was beginning to turn gray. He had slept on the floor of a house with twenty or thirty other boys. They were still asleep, sprawled on their blankets.

He heard the first twittering of birds in the woods. He heard dew dripping steadily from leaf to leaf of the trees. It spattered straight down to the ground.

The boy next to him rolled over and yawned. It was Little Fox. Blinking his eyes open, he whispered, "I'm hungry. Let's see what we can find to eat."

But Osceola shook his head. "This is a day of fasting, remember? It is Court Day."

Little Fox always had a big appetite. He got up on his hands and knees. "Not for women and children," he said firmly. "Only the men have to fast all day." He began to creep carefully around the tossed arms and legs of the other boys.

The two boys dropped to the ground. "I am old enough to go without food," Osceola said.

In the faint light, he could see his friend's face. He watched the expression on it. Little

Fox's big appetite was arguing with his wish to behave like a man. Appetite won. "I'm going to eat," Little Fox said. He began to make his way toward the place where his mother cooked.

Osceola too felt very hungry. But he made up his mind not to show it.

Now many people were stirring. A baby's voice wailed and Osceola heard the mother whisper to it. One figure after another slipped from a house to the ground. Osceola watched a woman crouch on her knees at her fire. She blew on the embers and laid pine knots on them. A tall, skinny boy dragged logs to another fire. Soon the whole camp was wide awake.

Before sunrise Osceola and a swarm of other boys from his village joined the throng moving toward the council square.

"Today people look different," he said to himself. "They are not gay. Everyone feels that this is a serious day."

He sat down in the quiet circle around the fire. When he saw Panther, he lifted a hand to attract his attention. Panther stepped around other people and squeezed himself in beside Osceola. The boys had become good friends.

Osceola nodded his head toward the row of twelve men who sat in the place of honor at one side of the fire. They were medicine men from several villages.

"There's old Shooting Star from my town," he whispered. "See, the one at the end."

Looking very dignified, all twelve sat cross-legged on hides. The boys looked eagerly at the chief medicine man in the middle of the line.

"I see it—the sacred medicine bundle," Panther whispered. "It is lying in front of him, wrapped in a white deerskin."

Osceola stared in awe at the bundle. The chief medicine man kept it hidden in a secret place all year except on this one day.

"He will open it just as the sun rises," Panther whispered.

"From here we will be able to see what's inside," Osceola murmured.

Someone poked him in the back to make him be silent. Feeling guilty to be the only one talking, he turned his eyes toward the east. There! The red rim of the sun just showed. His gaze flew back to the medicine bundle.

In the deep silence, the chief medicine man stretched out his hands. He unfolded the white deerskin slowly and carefully. He spread it flat. Many small objects were exposed. Each one was wrapped in buckskin.

Osceola stared hard. Everyone craned his neck to see. The small objects were called "medicine." They were believed to be God's gift to the Indians, given to the first Indian on the day he came up out of the ground.

Osceola knew that some of the medicine

consisted of horn, feathers, and stones. But he didn't know what all the things were. No one knew, except the medicine men.

Osceola listened carefully. He could hear

the old man murmuring about long life for the tribe. On purpose, the man talked too softly for anyone to catch all the words. Women and girls had to sit farther away than the men. Osceola knew they could not even hear the voice.

No one stirred a muscle. People seemed hardly to breathe. These were the most important minutes of the year in the life of the nation.

Then, under all those staring eyes, the medicine man wrapped up the bundle once more. It would not be unrolled again for another year. Carefully tied together, it would lie on view this one day. At sunrise tomorrow, it would be hidden away again in a secret place.

People began to stir and talk again. Panther turned his head and looked gravely at Osceola. "It is well for us," Panther said, "that the old men take such good care of the medicine bundle. If the medicine were allowed to die, the nation would die."

"I know," Osceola said. He was just as serious. "My grandmother says that our songs and dances and ceremonies are the things that keep the power in the medicine."

"True. We must not fail to have our scratches today," Panther said. "All men, from the oldest chief to the newest baby boy, must be purified this day by the scratch of a needle by one of the medicine men."

Osceola rolled up his sleeve. "You can still see a very small scar on my arm," he said, "from the scratch I took last year."

Panther inspected it. He said with regret, "My scratches have all been so small they left no scar at all. Even when there are no scars, the scratching ceremony helps to keep the strength in the Seminole medicine."

"So does the black drink." Osceola turned his head to look into the council house. He pointed to some young men who were handling the chiefs' dippers filled with a dark brew made from many herbs. "See, the chiefs are being served their first black drink now."

As each man drank, the young man lifted his voice in a long-drawn-out shout. Osceola listened with secret pride, because his own name had been taken from this "Yahola cry."

"When I am older," he said to Panther, "I expect to be one of the young men who serve the drink and give the shout."

Panther nodded. "We will have to take the black drink today too." He wrinkled his nose and smiled a little. "I wish it didn't smell so awful and taste so bitter."

Osceola said sternly, "But any man or boy who doesn't take the black drink will be sick in the coming year."

"I know." Panther was looking back toward the great fire. "Look—people are taking their places for the buffalo dance."

The buffalo dance was always performed after the ceremony of opening the medicine bundle. Then there were many other dances, and at noon it was time for a serious event. Law breakers were tried in court. Important matters that affected the whole nation were discussed by the chiefs and sub-chiefs.

"We can hear part of the talk," Osceola said, "if we sit very close to the council house."

The two boys made their way slowly through the crowd on the dusty council square. No dancing was going on now. Under the trees they had to step carefully over bodies curled up for naps in the shade. At last they sat down quietly in a group of other men and boys who had also come to listen. Osceola took off his shirt and rolled up his leggings to make himself as cool as possible.

A stocky, dark-skinned chief was speaking. "The general from the United States says that we must pay for their property that our warriors have raided. But the general makes no promise to pay for our property or to keep his people from raiding any more of our towns."

Chiefs and sub-chiefs and elderly warriors sat in a crowded circle on the council house floor. They were having a talk of grave importance, and so they had not removed their finery, even in the heat. Osceola was pleased to see that his old uncle wore the handsome cape, feathered in many colors.

"Many Indians, including women, have been killed by lawless Americans," said a scar-faced warrior sharply.

A sub-chief named Trout stood up to make a long speech. Before he started to speak, he looked the other men in the face one by one until he had their complete attention.

"You will not like my talk," he said slowly. "But I speak for peace. I believe we should

105

punish our young men if they attack any settlers. I believe we should move all our towns far from the United States border. We should retreat deeper into Florida and avoid conflict with the United States."

Osceola looked in astonishment at his friend Panther. What kind of talk was this from a fearless Seminole? Panther did not like the speaker's ideas either. He was scowling.

"Why should we obey an American general? We do not live in the United States," said another chief. He was so old that his voice quavered. "We left Georgia and came here to join the Seminoles in Spanish territory. The United States has no right to control our actions."

"They have no right, but they have the power," someone said hotly. "They want this land in Florida, and they will drive us away."

"Power!" rumbled a deep voice. "We have power! We have many guns and plenty of ammunition. The Seminoles could never be defeated by the United States Army."

The chiefs were excited, but they observed the rules of a council. Only one man talked at a time. At the end of his speech, everyone else was silent for a time, to show him courtesy and to think over his words. Now another voice spoke up. Everyone turned to the speaker.

"I have received word," this man said, "from a Creek chief who served in the United States Army. He tells me the United States may invade Florida to wage war on the Seminoles. If this is true, only one course will be open to us."

"We will go on the warpath!" someone cried out. Others gave grunts of approval.

Again Osceola's eyes met Panther's. This was the kind of brave talk they approved.

The chiefs debated on and on. The boys stole away at last to discuss all they had heard while they had a swim in the nearest lake.

At the Bee Tree

THAT EVENING Osceola played in the ball game as usual until someone called, "Now it's too dark to play any longer."

"We won tonight's game!" someone shouted. Laughing with fun, boys and girls began to trudge away from the ball ground.

Osceola pushed among the players and caught Panther's arm. "What are you wishing?" he asked. His eyes were twinkling with fun.

"I am wishing for my first ear of good, green corn," Panther said at once.

Both boys laughed. "All through the game, I could think of nothing but food," Osceola confessed. "It is nearly a whole day since I ate last. Come with me!"

They set off running like deer. They dodged around little girls playing ring-around-the-rosy and around men rubbing black drink on their bodies, as all the men had to do, to give them strength. They leaped over tree stumps.

As last they came to the fire where Osceola's mother was tucking ears of corn into the hot embers to roast.

"I want some of the boiled corn," Osceola said greedily. "Take some, Panther."

They fished floating ears of corn from her kettle of hot water. They began to chew away the kernels hungrily even though the corn was so hot that it burnt their tongues.

They hardly waited to swallow before they took up hot corn biscuits from a pan. Then they reached for more boiled corn.

Little Fox, who was standing near, watched

them. He switched his ball stick through the sand. "Next year," he said, "I will try to go without food too, like a man."

Osceola said kindly, "Next year you will be older. You will be able to go hungry, even when food is all around you."

When his first appetite was satisfied, Osceola was able to think of something besides food. He said to his mother, "Tomorrow the Green Corn Dance will be over. Then may I travel with Panther toward his town? He has marked some bee trees, and we want to get the honey. Afterward I will walk home alone."

"You may go," Gray Dove said. "I will give you a bag to carry. Perhaps you can fill the bag with honey."

"I will take bags, too," Panther said. "But let us carry no blankets or other supplies, except a little food. The nights are warm. We can sleep among the leaves."

110

Next day all the visiting Seminoles packed their belongings and set out on the trails to their own towns. Osceola and Panther traveled alone. They went swiftly across a level, green plain encircled with sloping hills. They passed a herd of deer, but did not stop to hunt.

On the second afternoon Osceola said, "I hear the lowing of cattle."

"Yes, we are on a white man's plantation."

Osceola said, "I thought the white farmers were angered when Indians cross their land."

Panther nodded carelessly. "They are. All white men have strange ideas. When they have paid money for some piece of land, they think that no one else is free to be on it."

"How foolish," Osceola said. "The Great Spirit gave all the land to all men. He did not parcel out bits of it to special people. But listen—is that the hum of bees I hear?"

"Yes. We are near the bees. Follow me."

Panther struck into a thickly wooded place. The air was heavy with the sweetness of flowering trees. Bees gathered nectar from these flowers. The boys walked across a thick green mat of pennyroyal. As their feet crushed it, a spicy smell, like mint, rose around them.

"Look there!" said Osceola. He stopped and pointed to a tall tree.

Thirty feet up its huge trunk was a hole. Bees were zooming in and out of it.

"And look there," he said. "And there and there." Many of the trees had holes, which seemed to be the homes of honey bees.

Panther slipped off his bow and arrow pouch and took a short-handled axe from his belt. He chose a bee tree with a slim trunk and began chopping at its base. The sound of his axe rang out clearly in the steamy air.

Osceola knew how to gather honey. While Panther chopped, he struck a spark with flint and steel and started a small fire of pine chips. Then he took a handful of rags his mother had given him. He wrapped and tied them around the end of a stick.

Soon Panther's tree was cut nearly through. It trembled, wavered, and slowly began to fall. The boys stood carefully out of its path. Its upper branches tore their way through the high growth of other trees. It fell faster and faster, and crashed to the ground.

Osceola dragged an armful of Spanish moss down from a nearby branch and rushed forward. "I'll stuff the bee hole with this," he said. "That will keep the bees inside."

Panther was chopping again at the fallen tree. A foot below the bee hole, he cut another opening in the trunk. Osceola set his roll of cloth afire. "Stand aside," he said. He thrust the smoky, smouldering stick into the new hole. He held it there and the boys waited.

"Now," Osceola said, "the bees inside the hollow should be stunned by the smoke." He re-removed his bundle of rags and put out the fire by rolling the bundle in the sand.

"I hope we find a lot of honey," he said hungrily. He put one hand carefully into the hollow of the tree. Bees crawled on his hand and arm, but they were so groggy from smoke that they didn't sting him.

"Hurry up," Panther said. "Give me some."

Osceola pulled back his arm. He held a broken honeycomb in his hand. Golden honey dripped from it. He bent his head to the delicious mass and took bite after bite of honey. He spat out the wax. The boys stood by the tree, gorging themselves on the sweet stuff.

"How sticky I am! And thirsty too," Osceola said. "Come, let's fill our bags now." They stuffed honey into their fawnskin bags.

"This isn't enough to fill them," Panther said.

114

"I had better cut down another tree." He wiped his sticky hands on the mat of pennyroyal and set to work once more with his axe.

Perhaps he was careless this time. At any rate, he stood idly, looking up and waiting for the tree to crash down. He was very close to the line on which it would fall.

"Watch out!" Osceola shouted. "Move back!"

Panther stepped back, but he was too late. The falling tree struck him and knocked him down. He sprawled full length, and when the trunk thundered to the ground it lay across his ankle. He sat up dizzily.

"Ouch! Lift the tree away for me."

Osceola heaved with all his might. "I can't," he grunted. "It's too heavy for me." He thought for a moment. "I'll have to dig the earth from around your foot and pull you free."

He saw that Panther's left arm was scraped from shoulder to waist, but he did not express his sympathy. Panther, too, ignored his wound. If his trapped ankle hurt very badly, his expressionless face did not show it.

Osceola knelt down. He began to use the head of the axe as a spade, to make a hollow under Panther's foot. Then he looked up and his hands were still. He listened.

"A horse is coming," he said. "It's being ridden fast by someone who knows this wood." He dropped the axe and reached for his bow. He fitted an arrow to it and stood waiting.

A tall, scowling man in dusty jeans cantered into sight on a gray mare. He had been riding hard. His white shirt was stuck to his skin with sweat. He looked left and right, but the boys were so quiet he did not see them.

His glance fell on the trees which the boys had cut, and he spoke a sudden word of anger. He swung down from the horse, and one hand reached for the pistol at his belt.

116

Panther spoke up in a courteous voice. The man swung toward him. Then he noticed the quiet boy with a bow and arrow ready in his hands and the boy sitting on the ground.

He and Panther exchanged speeches. The man's voice was stern. Osceola was astonished. Panther knew how to speak English!

Suddenly Osceola said, "I know this man! His name is Irving. He visited our camp the first night we were in Florida."

"I know him too," Panther said. "He is a good friend to the Seminole. But he doesn't like it because we cut down his trees."

Panther shrugged. "I told him that there are always plenty of trees, but he thinks we did wrong because this is his land. White men have these strange ideas."

Mr. Irving thrust his pistol back into his belt. He bent over Panther's foot. The anger left his face when he saw that the boy was injured.

He looked at Osceola and made lifting motions with his hands. The boy laid down his bow and arrow and stooped beside the log. He and the man were able to lift the trunk enough so that Panther could pull out his leg. He winced with pain, but said no word.

Mr. Irving's pleasant face was full of concern as he bent over Panther's ankle. He picked up two broad pine chips from the ground which might be used as splints. Then he bound them carefully around Panther's foot and leg with two handkerchiefs. Finally he lifted Panther to the horse's back and started to lead the horse away. All the while he kept talking in a gentle voice.

"He is taking us to his house," Panther explained to Osceola. "He wants a white doctor to examine my ankle. Bring the honey bags and come along to his house."

A Strange House

MR. IRVING led the horse, and Osceola walked beside it. The Irving homestead was not far away. Osceola looked curiously at the white picket fence that surrounded the yard. He stared at two high poles, one on each side of the gate. A colored banner waved at the top of each pole.

Panther looked back at Osceola. "One is a Spanish flag because Florida belongs to Spain," he said. "The other is a United States flag because Mr. Irving is an American."

Osceola gazed at the two-story frame house. It had a shady porch around three sides. Periwinkles and blue bachelor's buttons bloomed in flower beds beside the steps.

Mr. Irving called orders to a servant, who ran to carry a chair out of the house. Panther slid down from the horse to the chair. He was carried into the house on it.

Osceola followed him into the house. He walked carefully because everything was strange. How dark it was! The walls came clear to the floor. There was so much furniture! There were things to sit on and things to lay your bow and arrows on and other things whose use he couldn't even guess. Pictures were all over the walls in big, golden frames. Cloth hung down over all the windows.

He thought of a bare, Seminole chickee, with no furniture at all, and he thought, "What a crowded place this is."

He stood bashfully near the door and watched. Panther was laid on a black leather couch. A woman in a gray gingham dress hurried in. The curls that were pinned behind her ears bobbed up and down as she walked.

"That's Mr. Irving's wife," Osceola thought. "She was on horseback that night at camp."

She was followed by two servant women. Mr. Irving and the three women bent over Panther. One hurried to get a basin of water to wash him. Another brought a cup of something for him to drink. Mrs. Irving bandaged his ankle.

Osceola thought, "They act as if he were a chief and they were his own family. They must be very kind-hearted."

Then a boy and a little girl ran in. "That boy," Osceola thought, "was at the camp, too."

He stared at the children's pink-and-white faces. The girl had strange hair the color of a yellow magnolia blossom. It wasn't straight like Seminole hair. It fell to her shoulders in curls, like the tendrils of a grapevine.

Now all the grown-ups hurried away on errands. The Irving children saw Osceola for the first time. He stood very stiff and proud, and stared at them without smiling. The Irving boy took a step toward him. He stopped shyly. Then he moved resolutely forward. He pointed to his own chest. "Me—George," he said.

The young Seminole looked at him gravely. He pointed to himself. "Osceola," he said.

George waved a hand toward his sister and told her name. "Ethel."

Osceola repeated the strange word. "Ethel."

Ethel giggled and spoke to Panther.

"She likes you," Panther said. "She wants you to sit down. Go ahead. She is trying to show you politeness."

Osceola backed up to a strange-looking stool with arms and a back, and sat down. He leaped up in a hurry! The thing had rolled under him. He looked quickly at the children, but they were not laughing at him. They were only watching him in the friendliest way.

"They call that stool a rocking chair," Panther explained. He pointed to other things in the room and gave their English names. "Table. Piano. Grandfather clock."

Osceola stepped up to the tall box. It made a strange noise. *Cluck—clack—cluck—clack.*

"Is it a kind of toy?" he asked.

"Yes. It tells how late it is."

This was so funny that Osceola had to throw one hand over his mouth to hold back a laugh. "Why don't they just go outside and look at the sun or the stars?"

"Their houses are full of strange toys," Panther said. He seemed to know a great deal. "That one they call a fiddle." He pointed to a delicate-looking box with wires stretched from end to end. It lay on the piano. "They make music with those things when they dance."

"Instead of using drums and rattles?" Osceola asked. "And what is this thing?"

"A book. There are marks on the paper inside. They tell a story."

Osceola wanted to see the rest of the house. He prowled into the center hall and walked to a back door. Here was another porch like the one in front, and he stepped onto it.

A washbasin stood on a bench, and there was a roller towel on the wall. Beside the towel was a strange picture in a tin frame. Osceola stepped up to look at it more closely. He saw a handsome, serious face topped with a blue turban. Loose black hair hung from under it.

"That's a turban like mine," he said. As he spoke the face in the picture moved its lips too. Osceola broke into a peal of laughter. "It's a look-into glass," he said. "I have heard of these things." He forgot that the Irvings could not understand his words.

George reached up to the looking glass and took it down from its nail. He put it into Osceola's hands. "Take," he said. "Gift."

Osceola did not know the words, but he understood the meaning. He nodded his head and tucked the looking glass under his arm.

126

Mrs. Irving appeared in the doorway. She smiled and made motions with her hands as if she were urging all the children to come inside. Cautiously, Osceola followed her in.

He stopped at the door of the room where Panther lay. "They want you to eat," Panther said. "You will not like the food. White men's food is always too salty. But you will have to eat to show good manners."

Mrs. Irving led Osceola across the hall. Here a long table was covered with a cloth as white as heron feathers. She pulled back a chair for him, but before he sat down, he looked for its legs. No more rolling chairs for him!

George and Ethel sat across from him and watched with lively interest. He ate all that Mrs. Irving had placed on the plate. There were turnips with butter, cold pork, gravy, and several tall, white biscuits. He ate with his fingers and mopped up gravy with pieces of biscuit. He liked his mother's food better, but he was so hungry he could eat anything.

Ethel laughed right out loud and pointed to Osceola's face. It was bulging with great big mouthfuls of food. George gave her a hard poke in the arm, but Osceola didn't mind her laughing. She was only a little girl, and all girls were alike. They laughed at everything.

When he finished eating, it was growing dark. He was half asleep when Mr. Irving picked up a lighted candle and led him upstairs. He took the boy into a room and pointed to a tall, narrow piece of furniture. He kept talking, but Osceola didn't try to understand the words. He did understand the gestures and smiles.

Osceola climbed up two steps and lay down on the thing. For a moment he was alarmed. He seemed to sink down and down into blankets. It was like sinking into a million feathers!

As soon as Mr. Irving went away, Osceola

wasn't sleepy any more. He was homesick. He longed to hear wind in the trees and to hear frogs piping in the lake. "Only a crazy person could sleep on this soft thing," he thought.

He lay there, hot and uncomfortable, until the house was dark and quiet. Then he rolled out of that soft bed. In the darkness he felt his way slowly and carefully out of the room and down the stairs. He followed the sound of the box that went *cluck—clack—cluck—clack.*

Soon he crept into the room where Panther lay. He listened. He heard no other sound but Panther's breathing. With a sigh of comfort he lay down on the cool, bare floor beside Panther and fell fast asleep at once.

He woke at daylight. He sat up. "Panther?" he whispered.

"Yes?"

"I am going home. I think these people will take good care of you."

"They will. They say my ankle is not broken. After the doctor has been here, they will take me to my own village."

"Tell George I am leaving my bow and some of my best arrows for him, the ones whose tips are made of the scales of the garfish. I will take the look-into glass and the honey."

He crept out of the house and down the path. He opened the white gate and shut it softly behind him. Then he stood still and breathed deeply of the damp, cool air.

He laughed with pleasure to hear the crowing of a wild turkey cock from the top of a tree. It was answered by another call, and then by a third turkey in the distance.

A flock of flamingoes were flying slowly across the sky. It was not yet sunrise on the ground, but they flew so high that the morning sun polished their pink feathers to bright rose. He felt so free and happy that he began to run.

130

Soldiers Are Coming!

OSCEOLA looked into the mirror. He saw the face in the mirror break into a smile.

"Why! I remember the day I brought home this glass and hung it on the post of my mother's chickee," he said to himself. "Then I could see only my eyes in it. Now I can see my shoulders! I have grown that much in two years!"

Feeling very pleased with himself, he jumped to the ground. "Wait, Mad Possum!" he called. "I will go to the ball ground with you."

He ran after the young warrior. Mad Possum wore only a loin cloth. His skin was gaily painted, for he was to play in a big game.

131

He and Osceola strode to the edge of the village. A merry crowd of Indians had already gathered there. It was an exciting day. Men from a neighboring town had been invited to come to play a game of ball.

"In a few years I will be old enough to play the men's game," Osceola said proudly.

"But will you be tough enough?" Mad Possum teased. "Seminole ball games are rough."

"I know. In the last game, two braves were knocked out from blows on the head and another one had a broken arm," Osceola said. "Others must have had bruises. But all the players are too proud to show that they feel any pain."

"A fierce ball game is the most manly exercise I know," Mad Possum said. He swung his two ball sticks in his hands. "It is the next best thing to warfare itself."

Now they were pushing their way through the crowd at the ball field. Mad Possum gave a

132

great scream and leaped into the field. He threw both ball sticks high in the air and caught them as they came down. His friends cheered and waved. The Indians enjoyed his capers.

Players divided on the field. There were about twenty-five men to each team. Someone tossed the ball. Instantly the two groups swooped to the center. They yelled and swung their ball sticks.

"There goes the ball!" someone screamed. "A score! A score!"

But the ball sailed through the air and missed the post by inches. Osceola's townsmen groaned. The other side cheered.

The ball was in play again. Men were knocked down. Blood flowed from a cut on one player's forehead. A member of the opposing team staggered from the field. He was limping, but his face showed no expression.

"Catch it, Big Turtle!" Osceola shrieked.

Play surged to the sidelines. Onlookers backed up to make room for the players. Almost under Osceola's feet, Cloud scooped the ball into his sticks. He gave a mighty whirl. The ball soared toward the goal. *Thwack!* It hit the post.

"First score!" the onlookers shouted.

The teams divided into two groups again. In the moment's quiet, there came the tattoo of hoofs. Smiling faces turned toward the sound.

"It is some late-comer," a woman guessed.

A hard-riding Indian pounded out of the woods. He whirled his horse when he saw the crowd and thundered straight onto the ball field. He reined in so sharply that his sweating horse reared up on its hind legs.

"Put down your ball sticks!" he commanded in ringing tones. "The time for play is past! Andrew Jackson is leading a troop of soldiers toward the town!"

For a moment there was silence. No one

134

moved. Then men surged forward and sur-
rounded the messenger. Women backed away.
Their packed bodies moved almost like a wave.
Then the wave broke into individual women.

Some ran to collect their children. Others
hurried to cookfires to gather food. Some
jumped into houses and began piling clothing
into blankets that they rolled up tightly. All
knew that they must prepare for flight.

Osceola pressed into the throng of men who
surrounded the messenger.

"There are thirty horsemen, two miles away,
marching in formation," he was saying.

"Women and children can hide in the woods
south of here," the old chief muttered.

"We will creep up to the sides of the road
and ambush the soldiers," Howling Wolf said.

Mad Possum shook his head. "There is no
cover on either side of the road," he said. "We
will have to fight in the open."

The men began to scatter. Osceola caught Mad Possum's arm. "Some men will be killed," he said. "But what happens to those taken prisoner? Do Americans make slaves of prisoners?"

"No," Mad Possum said. "Prisoners are sent far to the West."

"West? What country is there?" Osceola almost had to run to keep up with Mad Possum.

"Strange country, that's all I know," Mad Possum said shortly. "We will fight to stay here. This is our home—Florida."

Osceola stopped and let Mad Possum hurry away to his own lodge. The boy looked all around. He saw a Negro woman strapping a basket of corn to her back. A young mother was fastening twin baby girls into a kind of cradle that she slung over her shoulders. Visitors and townsmen were forming into little family groups. Each person had bundles to carry.

"Osceola!" his mother called. "I need you."

136

The boy went to her chickee to help. If he were just a little older, he would be allowed to fight with the men, instead of having to be a helper. He wanted to be a warrior.

Gray Dove said, "White Heron and Shining Fish and six children will travel with us. But White Heron is ill and your grandmother is frail, so you must look after the youngest ones."

Osceola said, "First I will get my weapons." He hurried to the boys' house, where he slept since he was too old to live in his mother's chickee. He picked up his bow, saw that his quiver was full of arrows, and stuck a knife and an axe into his belt.

He returned to his mother. "Put one of the children on my back," he said.

Gray Dove lifted a small boy. The child clasped fat arms around Osceola's neck. Osceola hooked his elbows under the little knees. He twisted his head around.

"I am a horse for Short Hair, am I?" He began to caper to make Short Hair laugh.

But his grandmother said, "Save your strength. You will need it to carry the child."

Already many families had disappeared into the woods. Warriors had slipped away to meet the soldiers and give battle.

Gray Dove's little party moved into the forest. She went first, carrying a baby. Early Moon had grown lame in these months, and she limped along next. Behind the old lady went Shining Fish with a child slung on one hip. Poor White Heron had been sick with a fever for many days, and she stumbled along next. Three children followed, and last came Osceola.

"How slowly we move," he said to himself. "We stop so often to let White Heron rest."

Soon all the other parties were out of sight. An hour passed. Two hours. They trudged on and on. Now Osceola knew that his grandmother had been right. Short Hair seemed to drag more heavily on his back with every step.

Suddenly he stopped, listening sharply. "Rifle shots," he said. "Do you hear them?"

Everyone sat down on the ground. They were glad to rest. They listened.

"The shots are coming closer," Osceola said. "Now there is shouting. Do you hear voices?"

"No," said Gray Dove wearily. "Your ears are keener than ours. But if the soldiers are close, we cannot all escape."

White Heron moaned. She shut her eyes and leaned her head against a tree trunk. "Go on without me," she whispered.

"We will," Gray Dove said. "Shining Fish and I can take the babies and go more swiftly."

"Do you see that fallen log?" Osceola said. "The four children and White Heron and the grandmother must lie down behind it."

He seized White Heron's wrists and pulled

her to her feet. "Come, lie flat on the ground and I will cover you."

Gray Dove watched her son pushing and leading the sick woman and the grandmother and the children into hiding. She nodded.

"I leave them in your care," she said. "When all is safe, I will come back and give a signal. Answer no one but me!"

She shifted the baby from her back to one hip. She walked away without a backward glance. Shining Fish followed silently after her. She was carrying her youngest child.

For just one moment Osceola wanted to run after his mother. How much safer it would be to keep walking than to lie here and hide! But at once he knew he must act like a man. He had six people in his care.

Short Hair began to whimper. "Be still," he said sternly. "Lie down and I will pile dead leaves over you."

"But I'm hungry," a small voice said.

"So am I," Osceola said briefly. "But pretend you are a baby partridge hiding from a hawk."

While he joked and encouraged the children, he heaped dry leaves and dead branches over all of them. He tried to make the hiding place resemble litter blown there by a strong wind.

"I am leaving my footprints all around," he thought anxiously. "I hope the soldiers are not good woodsmen."

He stopped with a bunch of Spanish moss in his arms. "They are coming," he whispered. He took just enough time to scatter the moss across his own footprints and dived for cover. He snuggled close against Short Hair. He wondered if his back showed through the drift of leaves.

"I want a drink," a little voice said.

"Be quiet!" Osceola commanded in a fierce whisper. "The soldiers are near."

At once the children were still as field mice.

A Raid Is
Planned

Two HORSES walked to the left of the hiding place. The creak of leather harness and the faint jingle of chains told Osceola that they were soldiers' horses, not Indians' horses.

They moved out of hearing. The people hiding behind the log still lay quiet. The tip of a branch scratched Osceola's neck, but he dared not wiggle away from it.

Three more horses walked near. This time they were on the right side of the log. Would they notice the drift of leaves and branches? No—they moved on. Osceola heard low voices. Were the soldiers reading Gray Dove's trail?

The men were gone, but still the Seminoles dared not move. Osceola heard White Heron's rapid breathing. He knew she was in a feverish sleep. When a child squirmed, Osceola whispered sternly, "Quiet!" The child was still again.

Hours passed. The boy longed to move. The ground was damp and chilly. His left arm was numb where his weight lay on it. But if he squirmed, the children would stir too. They must all lie as motionless as possible. Soldiers might be prowling nearby on foot.

Osceola may have fallen asleep. After a long time, he was dimly aware that he heard the mourning call of a ground dove. What a strange bird, to keep calling so late in the evening. He listened sleepily. *Woo-oo*, it went. *Woo-oo*.

Then his thoughts cleared. His mother had said she would give a signal, but she had forgotten to name the signal. Her name was Gray Dove. Was she giving the dove's call?

He lifted his head carefully. He tried to make an answering call, but his mouth was too dry. He wet his lips and swallowed and tried again. "*Woo-oo*," he croaked. He had to grin. Any Indian would know that was not the voice of a real dove! Would the white men know?

There was a crackling of underbrush and a swish of garments. "Where are you?" Gray Dove's voice called softly.

Osceola wriggled out of hiding. "Here we are!" One after another, the children's heads popped out of the leaves. Even in the half-dark, Osceola could see dry leaves sticking in their hair. One little girl had a trail of Spanish moss around her shoulders like a shawl.

"Are you safe?" Gray Dove bent over them. "All of you? That is good."

She helped White Heron rise unsteadily to her feet and said to Osceola, "The soldiers found some of the families and took them prisoner.

But Shining Fish and I hid at the edge of a river. We lay under water with just our faces out. Even the babies were quiet while we held them in the water until the soldiers went by."

"I'm hungry," one of the children said.

Gray Dove laughed softly. "We can eat now. Follow me. We are making camp in a swamp a mile or two away. There will be no fire, but we have plenty of koontie."

Gray Dove led the way. She slipped an arm around her mother's waist to help her along. White Heron leaned on Osceola. The children straggled along after them.

Osceola murmured to his mother, "I wonder how the warriors fared in the battle. I wish that I could have been with them."

Gray Dove looked back. "I am glad you were here," she said quietly. "You took the part of a man today, and I am proud of you."

Osceola gave no sign that he was pleased at

these words. "I wonder too what became of our town when the soldiers invaded," he said.

The Indians hid in the swamp for many days. The first warrior from their village who found them was Black Snake. He was grimy from days of travel. He wore a bandage around one leg, where a bullet had nipped it.

"What happened in the battle?" Osceola asked at once. "Where are our braves?"

"Three of our braves were killed and four taken prisoner," Black Snake said. He looked around the hidden encampment. The women had built shelters of branches and bark. They had made cradles for the young children by tying skins between trees. They had found food.

"You can build cooking fires now," he said. "The soldiers are far away, at St. Mark's."

"Can we go back to our village?" Short Hair asked. "I miss our village."

Black Snake laughed shortly. "There is noth-

ing to go back to. All the houses are burnt to
the ground. The stores of food are scattered.
The gardens are destroyed."

"Then we will build a new town," Early
Moon said. She was an old woman, but she
was undaunted by hardship. "My grandson has

been exploring. He has told us of new land south of here. It is a place beside a river, far from any white settlement."

Several families came to join Gray Dove's camp. Little Fox's family was one of them. His father had returned safely from the battle, though many of the other men were wounded.

"But all the warriors are determined to go on fighting," Little Fox said.

"Of course," said Osceola sternly. "They will fight until every man is dead or imprisoned. We are fighting for our homeland."

One by one the families moved to the new campsite that Osceola had chosen.

"I see we are not building so many houses as we had before," Osceola said to his mother.

Fat Squirrel added, "Isaac says the Negroes are not sowing very large gardens."

Gray Dove nodded. "That is true. And every woman here has her belongings and a supply of food packed close by. Who knows? We might be attacked and have to flee again."

Osceola and Fat Squirrel were standing side by side, pounding a new supply of koontie in a log. When his mother was out of hearing, Osceola said to the girl, "My one wish is that the war will go on long enough for me to join the fighting. I will soon be of fighting age."

The Seminoles did not form a single army. Their chiefs did not make a general plan of war. One little band would raid a solitary homestead. A larger unit would surround a settlement and attack it at daybreak. A group would lie in ambush and snipe at troops on the march. Then the warriors would melt into the forests and the soldiers were helpless to pursue them.

One day Osceola lay on the rough floor of a chickee. He was listening to the hard summer rain beating on the roof and watching Mad Possum clean his rifle.

"We have a great advantage over the soldiers," the boy said contentedly. "We know the country. We know where to hide. We know the best places to cross the streams."

"True. And the soldiers are such poor trackers they cannot even follow us, unless they are guided by their Indian allies." Mad Possum spoke cheerfully as he rammed a piece of cloth down the chamber of his rifle.

Howling Wolf, who was a more serious person than Mad Possum, happened to be passing by and heard these words. He stopped and laid one hand on a post of the house while he talked. "You forget that the Americans have one great advantage," he said seriously.

"What is that?" asked Osceola.

"They have many, many people," Howling Wolf said somberly. "If fifty soldiers are killed, their government in Washington can send a hundred more, or five hundred more."

"That is true," said Mad Possum. "When our braves are killed, we cannot replace them. Boys do not grow very fast," he said teasingly to Osceola. "You must grow faster."

"If we steal five of their rifles, they can send new ones," Howling Wolf went on. "They can manufacture powder and shot."

"But we have another thing in our favor," Osceola argued. "We know how to live on the land. We can make or grow almost all we need."

"Yes, but sometimes our crops fail," Howling Wolf said. He stepped into the house and sat down cross-legged on the floor. A puddle of water spread around him as rain slid from his back. "Sometimes a village is destroyed, with all its corn and flour. What then? Why, Seminoles go hungry."

"But yesterday," Mad Possum said, grinning, "a band of Seminoles destroyed a whole settlement on the East coast."

152

"I know," Howling Wolf said. "By next week the people who are left will have a new supply of food. It will be sent down easily from that rich country up north, the United States."

"You are right," Mad Possum agreed. "They always seem to have all the supplies they need, but we need not be alarmed. In the end we will win. We are fighting for our own country, and so we will fight harder."

Howling Wolf asked, "Are you going with me and the other braves tonight?"

Mad Possum said, "Yes," and Osceola asked eagerly, "Are you planning a raid? Where?"

"On an American plantation many miles east of here." In spite of his respect for the enemy, of course, Howling Wolf would go on fighting. He stood up in one graceful motion.

"The farm has many cattle we can use. It is the place with two poles by the front gate and bright-colored cloths tied to them."

The rain stopped during the evening. Osceola lay down to sleep with a deerskin between his body and the ground. He lay with his chin on his crossed arms and watched the men silently gather at the edge of the clearing. Moonlight gleamed dully on their rifle barrels and glinted on tomahawks. They moved almost without a sound, as if they were near the enemy already.

When they slipped out of sight, Osceola thought, "I wonder what those colored cloths look like. Perhaps they are like the two flags Mr. Irving keeps at his front gate."

Suddenly he sprang to his feet. "I believe they are Mr. Irving's flags!" His heart was pounding hard. "The warriors are going to attack the Irving plantation!"

At once he knew what he had to do. "All white people are the enemy of the Seminole," he said to himself. "But the Irvings were friendly to me, and I must save their lives."

154

Osceola Gives Warning

Osceola looked up at the stars. How lucky for him that the night was clear! He would have to circle around many lakes, and he might follow paths that would curve. But if he kept his left cheekbone pointing at the Great Star, he would travel in about the right direction.

There was no time to lose. "The warriors know the quickest way," he told himself. "And they started before I did. Yet I must reach the Irving homestead well ahead of them."

He moved through the woods at a fast walk. A light breeze stirred palm leaves and made them whisper dryly. He smelled the gentle sweetness of tulip trees in blossom. Ahead of him he saw the dark shape of a raccoon moving silently across his path.

Osceola worried. "I cannot speak English," he thought. "Yet I must explain that there will be no use trying to battle the Seminole. The warriors will set fire to the buildings. All will be killed if they try to fight."

He circled a small lake. The moon threw her silver path across it, and the water rippled where a fish jumped. Beyond the lake was a wide, open plain. Here he began to run—not too fast, because he must not tire himself too early in the journey. He tried to run smoothly so that his weapons and his pouch of dried meat would not bounce against him.

Rather crossly he thought, "I wish I had rubbed myself with spoiled fish oil. The bad smell would drive away mosquitoes. How they cling and bite!"

156

He entered a forest, but in half a mile the ground became marshy. He had to retrace his steps and circle widely around the soft ground.

"I am losing time," he thought anxiously. "I will fail unless I arrive long before the warriors do. It will take time for the Irvings to dress and prepare their horses. They must be gone and far away before the braves slip near and surround the house."

He walked up sandy hills and ran down them. He stopped at the edge of a creek. He looked longingly at the opposite bank. It was so close, yet he dared not swim across. He saw alligators prowling on the banks, and knew many more were swimming out of sight. They did their hunting at night. He had no time to fight alligators. Again he turned from his course and ran.

On and on he jogged. Only a strong and healthy person used to hard exercise could have traveled hour after hour as he did:

"I am nearly there," he said at last. "I remember that lake with the dead oak tree at the north end of it. I passed it the morning I walked home with my look-into glass."

Now he was only a mile from the Irvings'. Daylight was two hours away. Would he arrive in time? Was Howling Wolf's band far behind him? Perhaps they were even ahead of him.

"But they had no reason to hurry as I did," he assured himself. "They may have stopped to rest. Surely I will get there first."

The going was easier now. He hurried over level, sandy ground. Soon he saw a house, black against the sky. Yes—just inside the fence were two poles. No flags hung on them now, but he felt sure they were the landmarks that Howling Wolf had mentioned.

He stopped and pressed his body close to the trunk of a giant magnolia tree. He listened. He heard a light, whispering noise. Was that the sound of human bodies walking lightly in the woods? No. All he heard was the rustle of a rabbit hopping among pine needles.

The tree trunk that he hugged was the last bit of shelter between him and the house. Ahead was cleared land. Then there was the white picket fence. It had a ghostly look in the dim light. Beyond it was the house.

"I will make a dash for it," he decided. "If the Seminoles have already surrounded the house, they will fire at me. They will not know who I am."

Osceola was brave, but it took all his courage to take that first step away from the magnolia tree. Then he ran. He ran like a deer, fleet and light. Like a deer he vaulted right over the fence. He had no time to stop for unfastening the gate. At the sound of a rifle or the *whishhhhh* of an arrow, he was ready to throw himself flat on the ground.

The only sounds were the pat-pat of his own feet and the hammering of his heart. He took the steps in one leap, sprinted across the porch, and flattened himself against the door.

"The braves must not be here yet," he thought. "If they were, they would have fired."

His next problem was to rouse the Irvings. He scratched on the door and rattled the doorknob. Nothing happened, so he moved to the front windows and tapped on the glass. Still everything was silent, so he began to look about the yard. Did he see figures beyond the fence? At first he thought not, but by now the moonlight was dimmer, and he could not be sure. He watched carefully.

Again he rattled the doorknob and waited. There—at last he saw a pale gleam of light through the glass in the door. It grew brighter. Someone was coming down the stairs with candle in hand. A bolt was slipped back, a key turned. The door opened. He was staring into Mr. Irving's puzzled, sleepy face.

At once, Osceola blew out the candle. He pushed into the house and shut the door.

"Seminole," he said rapidly. "Go! Go! Take young people and run to the settlement!"

Of course Mr. Irving could not understand. All he knew was that a crazy Indian boy woke him in the middle of the night, pushed into the house, and started to babble in the dark. He began to talk soothingly in English.

Mrs. Irving came down the stairs. She wore a ruffled nightcap and a blue robe that billowed all around her. The candle in her hand gleamed on a frightened face. Osceola did not mind having a candle now that the door was safely shut. He explained, using sign language too.

"Around the house," he said, and swung in a circle with a finger pointing outward. "Many braves." He held up all his fingers, outspread, to show how many. He snapped an imaginary rifle to his shoulder and said, "Bam! Bam!" He pretended to shoot an arrow.

The Irvings watched him as if he were acting a play. George and Ethel came halfway down the stairs. The little girl was blinking and smiling sleepily. Osceola rushed up a few steps to George. He whipped his knife from his belt with one hand. With the other he seized George's tousled hair. He made a slicing gesture with the knife as if he were scalping George.

That did it. Mrs. Irving fell into her husband's arms with a faint scream. George looked rather pale. They all knew, now. They chattered excitedly and Ethel began to cry.

"Go!" said Osceola. "Go!" It was the only word of English he knew.

Mr. Irving gave orders. He herded his family upstairs. Osceola remained by the door, listening. Feet were running, up there, and he heard

162

new voices, as the house servants were roused. Something, perhaps a trunk, was being dragged across the floor.

Mr. Irving ran downstairs again, buttoning his shirt. He hurried out the back door and Osceola followed. Mr. Irving ran to the stables.

"Good. He will wake the field hands and saddle the horses," Osceola said to himself. "I have done all I can."

He flitted across the yard, as quiet as an owl. "If I try to go home now," he thought, "I might meet the warriors. I will hide."

In the woods, he studied one tree after another and chose a tall palm with a thick cluster of leaves at the top. He climbed up.

"No one can see me here," he said to himself, "unless I go to sleep and fall like a coconut." He lay very quietly among the branches. What a long time the Irvings took to get ready! A Seminole family could slip away from a village in half the time. The horses were so noisy! They stamped and jingled their bits. He heard the low, frightened voices of field hands.

"Mrs. Irving and the children are coming out. Now Mr. Irving is putting them on horseback. House servants are mounting too."

A dark figure ran back to the house, as if to get some forgotten treasure. A horse neighed. Someone was crying softly. Osceola's hands were clenched in worry. The warriors would come at any minute.

"At last they are setting out!" he said to himself. "Four—five—six horses."

The horses were bunched together. They tossed their heads nervously and pawed the ground. In a restless pack they pushed through the barnyard gate and then strung out on the road. Long after they faded into darkness, Osceola could hear galloping hoofs. He heard voices in the stableyard, too, and saw flitting shadows.

"Of course," he thought. "There were not enough horses for all. But the field hands are not much afraid. They will hide in the woods and later join the Indians. Negroes are freer living with us than with their masters."

At last all was quiet. It was so quiet that Osceola nearly fell asleep in his high nest. He was startled wide awake by the sharp click of metal. It sounded like the cocking of a rifle. It *was* the cocking of a rifle!

The faintest light of dawn had appeared while he drowsed. He saw that his friends had come. Warriors lay flat on the ground, facing the house. Each one was sheltered by a tree stump or a fence post.

Osceola heard the crow of a turkey—in Howling Wolf's voice. It was a signal. Six or eight rifles cracked. A flaming arrow sped through the air. It bit into the roof of the stable. Wooden shingles caught fire. Two warriors

166

raced toward a pen where cattle bellowed and milled around in a frightened pack. The shrill whoop of an Indian cut the air.

"Now is my time to get away," Osceola thought, "while the braves think only of battle."

He slid down from the tree and slipped into the woods. He crouched low and darted among tree trunks. Farther and farther he ran, away from the Irving place. He knew that if he ever came back, he would find nothing but ashes and stacks of brick where fireplaces had stood.

"It is right that the farm should be destroyed," he thought. "If settlers cannot let us alone in our own country, they must go."

He knew that if the Indians found out that he had warned the Irvings, they would call him a traitor to the Seminole.

"But Mr. Irving was my friend," he said to himself. "It was my duty to save his family." He jogged on toward home.

Osceola Becomes a Leader

OSCEOLA did not get his wish. The fighting lasted only about a year. It ended in 1819 when a treaty was signed between the United States and Spain. The treaty ceded Florida to the United States. It was not yet a state, and was known as the Florida Territory.

Years passed and Osceola grew to manhood. "We live in troubled times," he said to his old friend Panther. The two young men met while both were traveling to an important meeting at Fort King. They were part of a large party of chiefs and warriors, going to meet with United States government officials.

Panther said angrily, "There will never be anything but trouble between the Seminole and the government. We will never forgive the white men for taking our best lands and building farms and cities on them."

Osceola nodded gloomily. "These reservations they have forced us to occupy——" he waved one hand toward the bleak swamp behind them—"most of that land lies under water in the rainy season. In the dry season, the ground is so barren it will not grow crops. There is hardly enough dry space for our villages to stand on."

Panther said, "My old parents died of starvation the year after the fighting. Some in my town survived, but they did so only by getting a little food from the government."

"By begging!" Osceola said. "The proud Indian who once owned all this country—he *begged* food from the newcomers to keep from starving! It is an insult!"

His stern face scowled in anger. He had grown to be a man of sturdy figure, not very tall, but muscular and erect. He was dressed now in all his finery. Over his knee-length hunting shirt he wore a loose jacket of flowered cotton. He wore a beaded belt.

Three black and white ostrich plumes nodded from the back of his headband. Long earrings hung from his ears and three half-moons of silver lay on his chest like a heavy necklace. He looked powerful and handsome as he strode along the sandy path.

"Some of the chiefs are weakening," Osceola said. "They are tired of resisting the government. They are willing to agree today to move all their people to the West."

Panther said, "I think the Great Father in Washington will have his way. He wants to push the Seminoles clear out of Florida. I think he will force them to leave. He wants all of us

170

to move far to the west, clear beyond the great river they call the Mississippi."

"Never!" Osceola exclaimed. "I talked last night to the head chiefs. I made them listen to a warrior's talk."

Panther looked at him in surprise. "You argued with the chiefs? You are only a young man, a sub-chief."

Osceola nodded grimly. "They listened to me. In time of danger, it is the young men who become the leaders."

It was not many miles to Fort King. This was the spot where the city of Ocala was to stand many years later. There the chiefs and warriors marched inside the big, log stockade. Women and children of their bands pitched camp under the trees outside.

Men filed into the main log building. They seated themselves on benches facing a table. Half a dozen soldiers sat around the table.

The head chief of all the Seminoles had the place of honor in the center of the front bench. He was old, sleepy-looking Micanopy, and his heavy, beaded cape clashed softly whenever he moved his fat arms.

Osceola watched the chief look to left and right on the bench and then begin to lower himself heavily. Osceola slipped between two other men and sat down quickly on the left side of Micanopy. Older men looked at him angrily, because he was not supposed to sit next to the chief. Osceola wanted to sit beside Micanopy so that the chief would have to listen to his advice during the talk.

"That's the Indian agent," Micanopy grunted to Osceola. "His name is General Wiley Thompson. That one at the table."

Osceola nodded. "I know him." His alert dark eyes studied General Thompson.

The general was a firm-looking man of middle

age in dark blue uniform. Osceola's glance darted over the other officers and at the soldiers in dusty uniforms who stood with rifles in hand, watching the quiet Seminoles. He glanced to the back of the room and saw the curious faces of Seminole women, who were crowded together at the doorway.

When all the Indians were seated, General Thompson made a long speech. Everything he said was carefully translated by a Negro. Then an Indian rose to answer. Thompson replied. Another Indian spoke, disagreeing. Back and forth went the debate.

The general's keen eyes swept over his quiet audience. He said, "My friends, you have signed a treaty. You have agreed to go West. Now it is October. In the spring you must go."

One of the chiefs stood up to answer. "No," he said stubbornly. "It was not an honest treaty. The men who signed it were only saying *they*

173

themselves were willing to go West. They did not make a promise for the whole nation."

General Thompson spoke gently. "My brothers, the treaty is binding upon you. You are obliged to act according to its terms."

Chief Trout said sadly, "My band will go. We know we will have no peace in Florida."

Micanopy stirred his body sluggishly. He opened his mouth to speak. Osceola leaned toward him and put one hand warningly on the beaded cape. He whispered to Micanopy. The fat chief settled back as if confused by the arguments, and Osceola jumped to his feet.

"We will never go!" he said in shrill, ringing tones. "We have powder and shot and many rifles. We have brave warriors. We will fight in the forests and in the swamps until not one Seminole is left to resist."

He stamped one foot on the ground and folded his arms across his massive chest.

174

"This is our answer to your treaties!"

The white men who sat at the table were startled at hearing these defiant words from an unknown young man. Indians, too, looked at

175

Osceola in surprise. It was the first time he had ever spoken up in council.

When the long meeting broke up, and the Indians were making their way home to their villages, one young brave said, "Who knows? If Osceola had not spoken when he did, all the chiefs might have agreed to move to the West."

"He is a chief to follow!" said the other man admiringly. "With Osceola to lead us on the war-path, we cannot lose." This speaker had once been a boy called Little Fox. Now he was grown, and his man's name was Running Horse.

A year of tension and danger followed. White settlers were killed and their farms were burned. Slave hunters raided Indian towns. They seized Negroes whom the Seminoles insisted were free people, but the American law upheld the raiders. More councils were held, but everyone only became angrier. Both the Indians and the Americans knew open war was not far away.

In December, 1835, a large party of warriors hid in ambush. They waited for two companies of American soldiers who were marching to Fort King. At a narrow passage in the road where it was bordered by palmetto trees, they watched while the advance guard marched past.

It was followed by a team of oxen pulling a cannon. Next came a wagonload of supplies. After it marched the men, led by Major Francis Dade on horseback.

No man guessed that nearly two hundred warriors had rifles aimed steadily at their hearts. Suddenly the scream of a war whoop cut the air. It was a signal.

All the rifles cracked at once. Half the column fell dead or wounded in that first volley. A fierce battle followed, and when it was over, only three soldiers of more than one hundred had escaped.

The terrible Seminole War had begun.

The Second
Seminole War

A SCOUT was reporting to Osceola. "The soldiers are trying to find a place to cross the river," he said. "But the river is too deep and the current is too swift for them."

For two days Osceola's scouts had lurked on the outskirts of a marching army. There were seven hundred Americans in all. Some were regulars and some were Florida volunteers.

"I have a plan," said Osceola. "We will trap them into a battle where it suits us."

He and his warriors stood on the bank of a river. All were painted for the warpath. Stripes on their faces, arms, and bodies made them look

178

very fierce. The paint also made it harder for anyone to see these men when they stood quietly among trees or bushes.

They wore earrings, feathers in their headbands, and silver bracelets on their arms. Otherwise they were plainly dressed in stout leggings, moccasins, and trousers. It was a cool afternoon in December, so they had blankets slung over their bare shoulders.

Osceola said to them, "This is a good place for us to stage the battle. At this place the bank of the river is six feet high. It will be hard for the soldiers to climb. And behind us is the Wahoo Swamp."

The Indians smiled slightly. They knew very well what a great advantage they had when they fought in the swamps. They knew the paths. They knew how to leap from one firm spot to the next one. They were quick to hide behind a tree trunk or in a thicket of shrubs.

179

The soldiers wore clumsy boots and heavy clothing. They bogged down in mud. They floundered through swamps. They walked across open spaces where their blue uniforms made easy targets for a hidden Indian sniper. Also, their eyes were not used to seeing in the dim light of the jungle in the swamps.

"We will lure the soldiers across the river at this point," Osceola said. "All of our canoes are hidden, so they will not know we are here, waiting. We will put an old canoe on the opposite shore where the soldiers will find it. The canoe will be bait for our trap."

"There is a small canoe," one of the warriors said. "It is big enough for six or eight men. It is old and battered."

"Good. The soldiers will think it was abandoned there long ago."

Osceola turned to another chief. His name was Alligator, and he had been a leader of

180

warriors since Osceola was a boy. But now Alligator listened to the young chief with respect.

"Do you know the large, dry hammock that lies about two miles deep in the swamp?"

"I know it. The one that has three cypress trees growing almost together."

"Yes. Tell your warriors that is where we will carry the dead and wounded."

It was usual for Indians to make every effort to remove dead and injured fighters from the scene of a battle.

The two chiefs and a cluster of their followers stood talking over plans. They had about two hundred and fifty fighters, including thirty Negroes. But even though they were outnumbered more than two to one in the coming battle, they felt sure of victory.

"I hear soldiers," Osceola said. "It must be the advance guard. Listen! They have found the canoe. Hear them shout to their comrades."

181

At once all the Indians melted out of sight. Overhead half a dozen snipers hid in the tops of trees. They wrapped their bodies thickly in gray Spanish moss. If a soldier happened to look up, he would not see the Indian. He would never know that a gun was pointed down at him, resting in the notch of a tree branch.

One of the Seminoles in his treetop watched half a dozen soldiers climb into the old canoe. He grinned to see how pleased they were. They thought it was a stroke of luck to have found a way to cross the river. They never knew they were falling into a trap.

The boat made trip after trip. It carried six or eight men each time. Hundreds of men lined up on the far shore, waiting their turn. More and more of them came noisily across. The Indians waited patiently and silently. Osceola would decide when to start the attack.

Finally, after much hard work, about two

hundred men had made the crossing. Suddenly Osceola's shrill and terrifying war whoop ripped into the air. Rifles spattered. Soldiers threw themselves flat on the ground and searched for Seminole targets.

"Bring back the boat! More of us will cross!" someone yelled.

Soldiers shouted and Indians whooped. They sheltered behind scrub pines and fired at each other. They met in hand-to-hand combat, using rifle butt against tomahawk.

A soldier heard the spat of a rifle overhead and fired at it. A warrior tumbled from his perch, wounded. Another soldier, struck in the leg, tumbled backward over the river bank and found himself sitting dizzily in the water.

Out of sight, a wounded Indian sank to his knees and found blood pouring widely down his arm. He clapped a handful of wet earth to his wound to stop the bleeding.

General Duncan Clinch ordered a bayonet charge. "Into line!" he shouted over the blasts of gunfire. "Trail arms—quick time—double quick—six paces extend—charge!"

A line of foot soldiers emerged with fixed bayonets. The Indians retreated. They disappeared in the timber.

"They've given up!" Clinch panted. "We'll chase them!"

But Osceola and his men hadn't given up. They formed a new position, farther from the river. They renewed their attack from hidden places. There was a second bayonet charge, and a third. Each time the Indians scattered, but each time they re-formed and attacked again.

With each yard that the soldiers fought into the swamp, the more hampered they were by mud and by the dim light.

"It'll soon be dark," General Clinch said to a major. "We've got to get our men back across the river. They'll be slaughtered if we spend the night in the swamp."

A bugler sounded retreat. Soldiers began to move back to the river. The battle was over with no great victory for either side.

Osceola had timed the battle to start before he had to engage the entire force. Therefore, fewer than half the soldiers had been able to get into the fight. About sixty of them were killed or wounded. Only half that many Indians were hurt or killed.

The war went on and on. The Indians fought very few pitched battles, like that one. More often they lurked out of sight and fired from ambush, or they attacked a camp at daybreak.

They always scattered before the soldiers could form up to give battle. Sometimes troops marched to a spot where they expected to attack the enemy, only to discover that a small group of Indians was attacking them—from the rear.

General Thomas Jesup commanded the American forces in Florida for several years. He said wearily, "The difficulty isn't to fight the Indian. It is to find him."

A soldier said, "An Indian is like a mosquito. When you try to slap it, it isn't there."

Sometimes warriors were captured. Often a village deep in the swamps would be discovered by soldiers. Women and children lived there secretly. They raised corn and tended livestock, to keep up a food supply for the fighters. The families would be rounded up and taken to the nearest fort as prisoners.

"Take them under guard to Tampa," Jesup ordered each time. "See that they have food and clothing, and ship them West on the next boat."

This is exactly what the Indians were fighting against. They did not want to be exiled from their homeland to the strange and terrifying country in Oklahoma.

"They must go," said the Americans. "Until Florida is cleared of all Indians, we will never have peace here."

Years passed. The war seemed no closer to being won. Citizens were astonished at the fierceness with which the Seminoles fought for their right to live in Florida. The Indians were astonished by the might of their enemy—the numbers of the soldiers and the strange weapons.

"It is no use," said one chief. "I am going to surrender. All my warriors and the women and children and Negroes of my band are going to surrender too. The United States is too strong for us. We can hold out no longer."

"I will never give up," said Osceola firmly. "I would rather die in Florida than live in the West. I will yet be victorious."

"My wife and children have been captured and sent into exile," said the other chief gloomily. "Why should I stay here without them?"

188

"The people of my village are starving," said another brave. "The soldiers discovered the cove where our crops were raised. My people escaped, but the gardens were destroyed. All our horses and cattle were driven away. My people would rather surrender than starve."

Osceola stamped his foot. "Where are the brave hearts that swore to go on the warpath to the death?" he demanded in his ringing voice. "Let us never give in! The Great Spirit will lead his children to victory."

Osceola rallied the tired spirits of the Seminoles. Other chiefs, like him, refused to be discouraged by the power of the enemy.

But though Osceola never gave up, he never did know complete victory.

He was captured. Even before his capture, the brave fighter was very ill with malaria. He grew thin and his strength failed.

American soldiers took him as a captive to

Fort Moultrie, at Charleston, South Carolina. A large band of other captives were taken with him. There he was under the care of a doctor, and he was well treated. However, he came down with a case of quinzy, or severe inflammation of the tonsils. This illness finally led to his death in January, 1838.

Although he was an enemy, Osceola had become a hero to the American people. All over the country, people mourned his death.

"He was a great leader," said a soldier who had known him. "He had a kind of personal magnetism that made people follow him gladly."

"He was a clever general," said an officer ruefully. "I know. I fought against him. He could plan and carry out a battle brilliantly."

"He was a great enough man to know mercy, too," said another. "He often spared the lives of his enemies when he might have killed them."

A Seminole Negro overheard this remark. He

190

had known Osceola, and he said, "Osceola told his warriors, 'It is not upon women and children that we make war and draw the scalping knife. Let us act like men!' "

Osceola's name has been given to four counties in the United States, nineteen villages and towns, many streets, a lake, and a United States destroyer. Many people have been named for him, both white citizens and Seminoles.

The Seminoles are still a nation. After Osceola's death, the war dragged on for another four years. Several thousand Indians and Negroes were removed to Oklahoma, where their descendants live still.

At last the fighting in Florida dragged to a stop. The few Indians who stubbornly remained in Florida were simply allowed to stay. They withdrew deep into the Everglades. It is a jungle-like part of Florida where no white people cared to make settlements.

About three hundred Indians were left at the end of the Seminole War, and their descendants now number more than a thousand. The modern Indians live much as Seminoles lived in the time of Osceola. They still mingle very little with the non-Indian residents of Florida.

Osceola was buried at the main entrance of Fort Moultrie. Indians and white citizens attended his funeral, and a military escort fired a salute over the grave. The tombstone with his name on it bears words that are fitting tribute to the famous Seminole:

OSCEOLA

Patriot and Warrior

More About This Book

WHEN OSCEOLA LIVED

1804   OSCEOLA WAS BORN IN A CREEK INDIAN VILLAGE
        IN SOUTHERN GEORGIA.

There were seventeen states in the Union.

Thomas Jefferson was President.

The population of the country was about
5,310,000.

1804–   OSCEOLA LIVED IN SOUTHERN GEORGIA UNTIL
1825   1815, THEN MIGRATED TO FLORIDA.

Lewis and Clark explored the Northwest,
1804-1806.

"The Star-Spangled Banner" was written, 1814.

Florida was purchased from Spain, 1819.

The Monroe Doctrine was issued, 1823.

1825–   OSCEOLA LIVED ON A FLORIDA RESERVATION
1833   ESTABLISHED BY THE GOVERNMENT.

The Erie Canal was completed, 1825.

A bill, ordering all Florida Indians to move to
the West was passed, 1830.

Cyrus McCormick invented the reaper, 1831.

193

1833–   OSCEOLA AROUSED INDIAN TRIBES TO RESIST
1835   MOVING TO THE WEST.

The first steel plow was produced in America by John Deere, 1833.

The American Antislavery Society was formed to oppose slave trade, 1833.

The Department of Indian Affairs was established, 1834.

Seminole Indians were ordered to leave Florida for the West, 1834.

Samuel Morse invented the telegraph, 1835.

1835–   OSCEOLA LED INDIANS IN SECOND SEMINOLE
1838   WAR UNTIL TAKEN PRISONER.

The Alamo at San Antonio, Texas, was captured by Santa Anna of Mexico, 1835.

Sam Houston defeated Santa Anna, making Texas independent of Mexico, 1836.

Bank failures caused the country to suffer a severe financial panic, 1837.

The Supreme Court was enlarged, 1837.

The Underground Railroad was established to aid Southern slaves in escaping, 1838.

1838   OSCEOLA DIED, JANUARY 30, AND WAS BURIED
        WITH FULL MILITARY HONORS.

There were twenty-six states in the Union.

Martin Van Buren was President.

The population of the country was about
    16,175,000.

DO YOU REMEMBER?

1. Why did the Indians in Southern Georgia decide
   to move to Florida?
2. How did Chicadee and Little Fox have trouble
   rescuing Star along the way?
3. Why was Chicadee eager to have his name
   changed to Osceola?
4. How did the Indians choose a suitable place for
   a village in Florida?
5. What happened when the four strangers came to
   visit the Indian village?
6. How did Osceola help Mad Possum after Mad
   Possum was bitten by a rattlesnake?
7. Why did Mr. Sims and several companions come
   to see the Indian village one day?

8. Why did the Indians in council square discuss their problems with the government?

9. How did Mr. Irving help Panther after Panther was injured by a falling tree?

10. What did the Indians do when they heard that Andrew Jackson was coming to attack them?

11. How did Osceola save Mr. Irving and his family from being killed by the Indians?

12. What did Osceola say when General Thompson ordered the Indians to move West?

13. How did Osceola and his warriors fight during the Seminole War?

14. Where and how do the descendants of the Seminoles live in Florida today?

IT'S FUN TO LOOK UP THESE THINGS

1. How and where did the United States obtain Florida from Spain?

2. When was Florida admitted as a state in the United States?

3. Where are the Everglades and the Big Cypress Swamp located in Florida?

4. What are these regions like and why are they hard to penetrate?

5. Where did most of the Seminoles settle after they agreed to leave Florida?

6. What are Indian reservations and why have they been established in many places.

INTERESTING THINGS YOU CAN DO

1. Prepare a map showing where the Everglades and Big Cypress Swamp are located.

2. Collect photographs of the Everglades and Big Cypress Swamp for an exhibit.

3. Describe a chickee, or Indian house, such as the Seminoles built.

4. Dress a doll to show the costumes which the Seminoles wore.

5. Make a model of a Seminole village, similar to the one where Osceola lived.

6. Find out how the Seminole Indians live in Florida today.

7. Make a list of famous Indian leaders in our country besides Osceola.

OTHER BOOKS YOU MAY ENJOY READING

First Book of the Indian Wars, Richard B. Morris. Watts.

North American Indian Series, Sonia Bleeker. Morrow.

Our Indian Heritage, Clara Lee Tanner and Richard Kirk. Follett.

Pictorial History of the American Indian, Oliver La Farge. Crown.

Tecumseh: Shawnee Boy, Augusta Stevenson. Trade and School Editions, Bobbs-Merrill.

Trail to Oklahoma, Jim Booker. Broadman.

INTERESTING WORDS IN THIS BOOK

ambush (ăm′boŏsh) : attack from a hidden position

astonishment (ăs tŏn′ĭsh mĕnt) : surprise, amazement

boisterous (bois′tĕr ŭs) : noisy and gay

calico (kăl′ĭ kō) : cotton cloth printed in colorful figures

chickadee (chĭk′à dē) : small grayish bird found in many parts of the country

courtesy (kôr′tĕ sĭ) : respectful treatment

198

cypress (sī′prĕs) : evergreen tree with hard red wood widely used in building

defiant (dĕ fī′ănt) : resisting authority

delicious (dĕ lish′ŭs) : pleasing to the taste

descendant (dĕ sĕn′dănt) : offspring, as a son, grandson, or great-grandson

dignified (dĭg′nĭ fīd) : noble, with distinction

ember (ĕm′bẽr) : glowing coal still burning in the ashes of a fire

exile (ĕk′sīl) : person forced to leave his home or country

flamingo (flă mĭng′gō) : large white and scarlet bird with long legs and neck used for wading and feeding in water

garfish: kind of fish with long narrow body, elongated jaws, and hard, shining scales

herb (ûrb) : plant lacking a woody stem that grows and dies down each year

malaria (mă lâr′ĭ ȧ) : disease marked by chills, fever, sweating, and anemia, transmitted by the bite of the anopheles mosquito

melancholy (mĕl′ăn kŏl′ĭ) : sad, gloomy

monotonous (mȯ nŏt′ȯ nŭs) : without change or variety

nectar (nĕk′tẽr) : sweet liquid found in many flowers and gathered by bees

199

pennyroyal (pĕn ĭ roi'ăl) : sweet-smelling herb

plantation (plăn tā'shŭn) : large tract of land cultivated by laborers

pouch (pouch) : small bag

quinzy (kwĭn'zĭ) : severe inflammation of the throat, with swelling and fever

resentful (rĕ zĕnt'fŏŏl) : indignant, displeased

sapling (săp'lĭng) : young tree

slaughter (slô'tĕr) : kill, butcher

sniper (snī'pĕr) : person who shoots an enemy from hidden location

Spanish moss: plant with long, grayish, hair-like stems hanging from the branches of trees

swamp (swŏmp) : wet, spongy land

thatched (thăch'd) : covered with straw, rushes, reeds, or leaves for roof

treaty (trē'tĭ) : agreement between nations

tribute (trĭb'ūt) : praise, reward

warrior (wŏr'ĭ ĕr) : male Indian, trained to fight in Indian warfare

whooping crane: large bird with long legs and neck and powerful wings, noted for its loud deep call or cry

wince (wĭns) : flinch from pain, draw back from a blow